THREATENED MAMMALS, BIRDS, AMPHIBIANS AND FISH IN IRELAND

Irish Red Data Book 2 : Vertebrates

A. V

BEL

First published 1993

This Red Data Book
was edited for the
Department of the Environment for Northern Ireland
by
Dr J.K. Partridge

CONTENTS

LIST OF FIGURES

LIST OF PLATES

COLOUR SECTION

COVER

LIST OF TABLES

ACKNOWLEDGEMENTS

This Red Data Book has been compiled and edited with the assistance of a large number of people and the following are thanked for their generous contributions through the provision of information, discussion, constructive comment, guidance and advice. Apologies are offered to anyone inadvertently omitted.

C. Allan, D. Allen, P. Allen, R. Anderson, L.A. Batten, J. van den Berg, S. Berrow, T. Bradley, H. Brazier, P. Brennan, R.A. Brown, P. Buckley, J. Carson, T.D. Carruthers, S. Casey, W.S.T. Champ, R.A. Chapman, D.C. Cotton, J. Coveney, M. Crozier, B. Curran, G. D'Arcy, R.D. Davidson, H. Delaney, E. Dempsey, R. Devlin, E. Doran, J. Dunne, E. Fahey, K. Fitzpatrick, P. Fitzmaurice, S. Foster, R.J. Fuller, D. Gibbons, M. Gibbons, J. Good, B. Goggin, J. Greenwood, P. Grice, J. Harradine, R. Harrington, J. Harwood, S. Heery, I.J. Herbert, D. Hickie, J.P. Hillis, J. Hurley, C.D. Hutchinson, P. Hutchinson, E.Jones, K.W.S. Kane, B.P. Kavanagh, M. Kennedy, F. King, R. Langston, J.B. Larner, E.D. Le Cren, J.K. Lovatt, R. Lunnon, R. Luxmoore, A. Mackay, B. Madden, J. Magee, E. Mayes, H. McCann, N.D. McKee, D. McMahon, M. Marquiss, C. Mellon, O.J. Merne, D.H. Mills, R.T. Mills, C. Moriarty, R. Murphy, R.G.W. Nairn, B. M. Nelson, D. Norriss, Northern Ireland Bat Group, M. O Briain, J. O'Donoghue, C. O'Keefe, Ordnance Survey Office (Dublin), M. O'Sullivan, O. O'Sullivan, P. O'Sullivan, L. O'Toole, B. Ottway, K. Preston, D.T.G. Quigley, R.F. Ruttledge, L. Ryan, S. Ryan, C. Sargeant, C.R. Shawyer, J.R. Sheppard, D. Silke, C.M. Smal, P. Smiddy, M.C.D. Speight, R.E. Stebbings, S.M. Swift, A.P. Stott, D.A. Stroud, S.N. Stuart, M. Sweeney, M.L. Tasker, R.W. Turrell, E. Wallace, A. Walsh, P.M. Walsh, J.H. Wells, J. Whiteside, N.P. Wilkins, G. Williams, C.J. Wilson, I. Winfield, R.B. Wood.

Special thanks are due to the Steering Committee whose members gave generously of their time and expertise throughout the project.

The invaluable assistance of Gordon Young and Jim Lavery must be acknowledged for providing practical assistance with the computing element of the project; also, Richard Weyl who guided the project on behalf of DoE (NI) Environment Service, Dr Peter Maitland, Dr Ken Whelan and Dr Niall O Maoileidigh for advice on the fish; Dr Kate McAney for advice on bats; Deirdre Joyce for typing assistance and Gill Alexander for cartography. Comments on drafts were kindly provided by Dave Allen, Dr Bob Brown, Oscar Merne, David Norriss, and Gwyn Williams, as well as members of the Steering Committee. Special thanks are due to Marianne ten Cate who typed the original text and helped in many more ways besides.

Finally, I would also like to acknowledge the considerable contribution of Dr Karl Partridge who prepared figures and maps, obtained photographs, wrote accounts of a selection of extinct species and made editorial changes to some sections of my final draft.

STEERING COMMITTEE

J.S. Furphy, *Department of the Environment for Northern Ireland*
R.S. Weyl, *Department of the Environment for Northern Ireland*
H.J. Wilson, *National Parks and Wildlife Service, Office of Public Works, Republic of Ireland*
Dr. T.G.F. Curtis, *National Parks and Wildlife Service, Office of Public Works, Republic of Ireland*
Professor J.S. Fairley, *Department of Zoology, University College Galway*
Dr. J.K. Partridge, *Formerly Royal Society for the Protection of Birds, Belfast; Presently Natural Environment Consultants Ltd*
Professor A. Ferguson, *School of Biology and Biochemistry, Queen's University, Belfast*

ABBREVIATIONS

ASSI	Area of Special Scientific Interest
BTO	British Trust for Ornithology
CITES	Convention on International Trade in Endangered Species of Wild Fauna and Flora
EC	European Community
ESA	Environmentally Sensitive Area
IUCN	International Union for the Conservation of Nature and Natural Resources
IWC	Irish Wildbird Conservancy
IWF	Irish Wildlife Federation
IWRB	International Waterfowl and Wetlands Research Bureau
km	kilometre(s)
m	metre(s)
NI	Northern Ireland
RDB	Red Data Book
RoI	Republic of Ireland
RSPB	Royal Society for the Protection of Birds
SPA	Special Protection Area
UK	United Kingdom
UN	United Nations
UWT	Ulster Wildlife Trust
WWT	Wildfowl and Wetlands Trust

For abbreviations used in Summary Box in Species Accounts see pages 14–16

FOREWORD

We are pleased to welcome the publication of this Red Data Book, the second to be produced covering the whole of Ireland. It has always been accepted that the conservation of wildlife requires co-operation between Governments. The European Community has endorsed this view, through the Birds and Habitats Directives, and this book is a contribution to the information required to allow us to meet our obligations under those Directives. It also follows the lead set by the first Red Data Book for Ireland, for vascular plants, published in 1988 and more recently by the first in a series of Red Data Books for Britain and Ireland, which dealt with Stoneworts.

For many people, the most familiar animals are the vertebrates, comprising mammals, reptiles, amphibians and fishes. While these are the most well-known groups of animals, the conservation requirements of many species are poorly understood and action to conserve them is often difficult. Many species require large areas of land or water for their feeding or breeding range, and these may include areas heavily influenced by man. Subtle changes in human activity can often have dramatic effects as illustrated by the decline of several species listed in this book.

The Red Data Book will bring the conservation priorities of threatened vertebrates to a wider audience. We believe this is vital. Successful conservation of many species mentioned in this book will only be achieved through the co-operative action of several groups of people, including landowners, voluntary conservation bodies and Government Departments.

We commend this book not only to these groups, but to the wider public. The future of our wildlife is the responsibility of us all. Wildlife is part of our heritage, and of our legacy to future generations.

Robert Atkins MP

Minister for the Economy
and the Environment
for Northern Ireland

Noel Dempsey TD

Government Chief Whip and
Minister of State at the
Department of Finance of Ireland

PREFACE

The Irish Red Data Book for Vertebrates is the first comprehensive review of rare and threatened mammals, birds, amphibians and fish in Ireland. Its purpose is to provide basic information about these animals for all those engaged in wildlife conservation in Ireland and for those involved in framing wider conservation measures within the European Community. In addition, it is intended to draw to the attention of a wider audience the status of Ireland's rare and threatened vertebrates, in the hope that an informed public will be better equipped to promote and support wildlife conservation.

The Red Data Book is the product of a collaborative effort with input and direction from the Department of the Environment for Northern Ireland, the National Parks and Wildlife Service of the Office of Public Works, Republic of Ireland and several specialist advisers who served on the Steering Committee. The work is based on an initial desk review of the 230 vertebrate species which regularly occur in Ireland. The Red Data Book selection of 68 species was made using criteria laid down by the International Union for the Conservation of Nature and Natural Resources (IUCN). The 68 species comprise seven species which are extinct in Ireland, 42 threatened species and 19 species which occur in Ireland in internationally important numbers and are considered threatened in Europe. While these last-named 19 species are not given full treatment in this book, they are included as most Red Data Books now include this category in an attempt to fulfil national responsibilities for covering internationally-threatened species.

The selection of species included in this Red Data Book is not final, because implicit in the compilation of a Red Data Book is the need for regular updating and revision. The need for such updating and revision will be evident from the uneven treatment of the species which arises from the wide differences in the quantity and quality of information presently available. So, this Red Data Book is not an end in itself, nor anything like the full agenda for vertebrate conservation in Ireland. It is a beginning which can form the basis of a comprehensive Irish vertebrate conservation programme which could be undertaken, on a co-operative basis, by state, European and voluntary wildlife conservation agencies. In the interim I suggest that a Red Data Vertebrate Register be established to collect and collate records and information on Ireland's rare and threatened vertebrates on a continuing basis.

A.W. October 1993

1 INTRODUCTION

BACKGROUND

The concept of a Red Data Book was first proposed by Peter Scott in 1963 and later defined as 'a register of threatened wildlife that includes definitions of degrees of threat' (Scott *et al.* 1987). Although Red Data Books had precursors in several earlier books on extinct and vanishing animals it was not until the mid-1960s that the International Union for the Conservation of Nature and Natural Resources (IUCN), at Peter Scott's instigation, established internationally workable criteria and a generally acceptable approach to the presentation of information on rare and endangered plants and animals. Since then the IUCN has produced several Red Data Books and Red Lists of species threatened on a world scale. In addition, many countries around the world have produced their own Red Data Books and Red Lists. Some have adopted the IUCN criteria while others have adapted or developed these to suit their own national circumstances.

This Red Data Book is the second in a series produced on an all-Ireland basis. The first concerned Ireland's rare and threatened flowering plants, *Irish Red Data Book 1 -Vascular Plants* by T.G.F. Curtis and H.N. McGough in 1988. In addition, a series of Red Data Books for Britain and Ireland are currently being produced. The first of these, concerning Stoneworts by N.F. Stewart and J.M. Church, was published in 1992. A further publication on bryophytes is in preparation.

The subjects of this Red Data Book, the vertebrates, are animals with backbones. This, together with other characteristics, distinguishes them from invertebrates such as starfish, insects and worms. Five major groups can be recognised within the vertebrates - mammals, birds, reptiles, amphibians and fish. Mammals and birds are 'warm-blooded' whilst reptiles, amphibians and fish are 'cold-blooded'.

The *Irish Red Data Book for Vertebrates* is a summary of the currently available information about those vertebrate animals in Ireland which have been listed as rare or threatened to some degree or which have become extinct in the past 300 years. It describes the process employed in selecting the species, presents an account of the status of each species and considers the conservation issues which the Red Data Book selection raises.

VERTEBRATES IN IRELAND

Introduction

Ireland, compared with Britain and continental Europe, has an impoverished vertebrate fauna (Table 1). This reflects Ireland's isolated position at the western edge of the Western Palaearctic, the small size of the island, the restricted latitudinal range, and the more restricted range of habitats available (Hutchinson 1989).

This book had its origins in a Review of the 230 species of vertebrates which occur regularly in Ireland - on land, in freshwater and, in some circumstances, in coastal waters. Most of the species reviewed were birds and, as many are migratory, their inclusion required careful consideration. Although 403 bird species have been recorded in Ireland since 1900, only the 168 species which have (since 1900) regularly bred or wintered in Ireland or have been regular passage migrants were considered for inclusion, together with six species now extinct in Ireland.

TABLE 1 Ireland's vertebrate fauna compared with that of Britain and Europe (east of 30 °E longitude)

	Ireland	Britain	Europe
Mammals+	31	54[1]	167[1]
Birds*	141	210[2]	471[3]
Reptiles~	1	7[4]	85[4]
Amphibians	3	11[4]	45[4]
Fish (freshwater)	26	55[5]	215[5]

+ *Excluding cetaceans*

* *Regularly breeding species*

~ *Excluding marine turtles*

Sources: [1] *Macdonald and Barrett 1993,* [2] *Batten* et al. *1990,* [3] *Peterson* et al. *1983,* [4] *Arnold* et al. *1978,* [5] *Maitland and Campbell 1992*

Among the mammals, cetaceans (dolphins, porpoises and whales) have been excluded because there is insufficient information available on their occurrence, movements and ecology in Irish waters. However, they are animals which are threatened and should be considered in future revisions of the Red Data Book as more information about them becomes available. Species occurring in Irish waters are listed in Appendix I.

All the Irish vertebrates, except the Pollan*, occur elsewhere in Europe and many are widespread, if not common in the European Community.

* For scientific names of species see Appendices I and II.

Vertebrate Recording in Ireland

There is a long tradition of field natural history in Ireland which peaked around the turn of the century. From about 1910 until the mid-1950s there was little general interest in nature though there were several notable individuals, such as R.Ll. Praeger and C.B. Moffat who continued to study and write about Ireland's flora and fauna.

Amongst the vertebrates it was the birds which received the greatest attention from naturalists and this is the situation which prevails today. Much recording and field survey work on birds has been undertaken by members of the Royal Society for the Protection of Birds (RSPB), the British Trust for Ornithology (BTO) and the Irish Wildbird Conservancy (IWC), while the Wildfowl & Wetlands Trust (WWT) and the International Waterfowl and Wetlands Research Bureau (IWRB) organise international wildfowl censuses.

However, little amateur work has been carried out on the other groups, though with the advent of the Ulster Wildlife Trust (UWT) (formerly the Ulster Trust for Nature Conservation), the Irish Wildlife Federation (IWF), the Bat Groups and a number of smaller specialist organisations, horizons have broadened in recent years to take in mammals, amphibians and Ireland's only indigenous reptile, the Viviparous Lizard. However, fish still appear to be the preserve of professional biologists and there is little sign that amateur naturalists or anglers are prepared to contribute to the study of aquatic wildlife.

Professional research and survey work has been the responsibility of the Department of the Environment for Northern Ireland since 1965 and the National Parks & Wildlife Service in the Republic since 1970. In addition, the respective fisheries agencies undertake research and field surveys, but usually only on game or commercial species which are generally outside the scope of this book. The RSPB, BTO and IWC also undertake professional field studies as do a small number of staff and students in the academic institutions.

2 SELECTION OF THE RED DATA BOOK SPECIES

CRITERIA USED

Since the mid-1960s the IUCN has produced a series of Red Data Books on a global scale covering threatened mammals, birds, amphibians and reptiles, fish, flowering plants, and invertebrates. Since 1966 threat categories have evolved and up to ten categories have been used in recent global Red Data Books - Extinct (Ex), Endangered (E), Vulnerable (V), Rare (R), Out of Danger (O), Indeterminate (I), Insufficiently Known (K), Commercially Threatened (CT), Threatened Community (TC) and Threatened Phenomenon (TP) - although not all have been used in one book (Munton 1987).

With the development of national and regional Red Data Books the interpretation and use of the IUCN threatened species categories is now diverging widely and recent national Red Data Books have drawn up criteria and categories which better suit their own particular circumstances (see Batten *et al.* 1990; Osieck 1986).

In choosing categories and criteria for the present Red Data Book it was debated whether or not to use the IUCN criteria -they were never intended to be used at a national scale - or to devise specific national criteria, as some other countries have done. In the end, it was decided to remain with the IUCN criteria as these have been widely used and accepted internationally. (The IUCN is currently reviewing new methods for assigning threat categories (IUCN 1990)). As national Red Data Books should also reflect national responsibilities for protecting internationally-threatened species (Collar 1987) it was decided to include one non-IUCN category - Internationally Important. However, throughout the book threatened species have been kept separate from internationally-important species so that the prime function of the book - to highlight species threatened in Ireland - is not obscured. Only summary accounts have been prepared for the unthreatened but Internationally Important species.

The present Red Data Book uses five IUCN categories as well as the Internationally Important category and these are defined in Table 2 on page 6.

AREA COVERED

The Red Data Book covers the entire island of Ireland which includes Northern Ireland and the Republic of Ireland (see Map). The whole of the island is taken as one biogeographical unit and, historically, the fauna has been studied in that context. Although plants are studied on the basis of forty vice-counties (Curtis and McGough 1988) there is no such tradition for vertebrate animals and the smallest sub-units used in this book are the thirty two counties, six in Northern Ireland and twenty six in the Republic.

The European Community (EC) has been taken as the basis for the evaluation of Irish Red Data Book species in an international context. It is acknowledged that this is not particularly satisfactory in biogeographical terms. However, it is relevant in political and administrative terms (e.g. in the relation to the EC 'Birds Directive') and these are of immediate importance from the standpoint of practical conservation. It is also accepted that the boundaries of the EC may expand in the near future. However, regular revisions of the Red Data Book will be able to take account of these changes.

Once an internationally recognised biogeographical area has been identified and fixed for all classes of vertebrates and once there are sufficient data available for all species from all countries within this area (perhaps 'north-west Europe'), it should be used exclusively for the evaluation of the status of Irish species in an international context, rather than the area occupied by the EC.

TABLE 2 Red Data Book categories and criteria used in this book

EXTINCT (EX)

'Species not definitely located in the wild during the past 50 years' (Criterion as used by CITES).

Taxa* which formerly had wild breeding populations in Ireland but which are now believed to have died out.

ENDANGERED (E)

'Taxa in danger of extinction and whose survival is unlikely if the causal factors continue operating. Included are taxa whose numbers have been reduced to a critical low level or whose habitats are so drastically reduced that they are deemed to be in immediate danger of extinction.'

VULNERABLE (V)

'Taxa believed likely to move into the 'Endangered' category in the near future if the causal factors continue operating. Included are taxa of which most or all the populations are decreasing because of over-exploitation, extensive destruction of habitat or other environmental disturbance; taxa with populations that have been seriously depleted and whose ultimate security has not yet been assured; and taxa with populations that are still abundant but are under threat from severe adverse factors throughout their range.'

RARE (R)

'Taxa with small populations that are not at present 'Endangered' or 'Vulnerable', but are at risk. These taxa are usually localised within restricted geographical areas or habitats or are thinly scattered over a more extensive range.'

INDETERMINATE (I)

'Taxa known to be 'Endangered' or 'Vulnerable' or 'Rare' but where there is not enough information to say which of the three categories is appropriate.'

INTERNATIONALLY IMPORTANT (II)

Taxa which are common and/or widespread in Ireland but are considered to be Rare or Threatened in the European Community. These taxa are listed in Annex I of the Birds Directive and/or Appendix II of the Bern Convention and/or Annexes II, III and V of the Habitats Directive.

IUCN Note: In practice, 'Endangered' and 'Vulnerable' categories may include, temporarily, taxa whose populations are beginning to recover as a result of remedial action, but whose recovery is insufficient to justify their transfer to another category.

* Taxa (taxon, singular) = a general term for taxonomic groups, whatever their rank. In this book only the species and subspecies levels are used.

REVIEW OF STATUS OF IRISH VERTEBRATES

A full review of all Irish vertebrates was carried out to provide a systematic basis for selecting the Red Data Book candidate species. A database was compiled on the extant Irish vertebrates which included 31 mammals, 168 birds, one reptile, three amphibians, and 27 freshwater or estuarine fish. These species are listed in Appendix I. A data sheet was prepared for each species with information on Irish, European and World distribution, numbers, population trends, habitat, threats, conservation status, vulnerability, the quality and status of knowledge on the species, the Bezzel Index value (birds only, see below) and, finally, its potential for inclusion in the Red Data Book. Although not considered for inclusion in this Red Data Book, brief notes were also compiled on the status of 17 species of cetaceans which occur regularly in Irish waters.

A candidate list of extinct Irish vertebrates was prepared separately and from this a list of species which are reliably known to have become extinct in the past 300 years was drawn up.

All baseline data collected and collated for the preparation of the *Irish Red Data Book for Vertebrates* are held by the Environment Service of the Department of the Environment for Northern Ireland with summary data for each species on dBase III in Apple Mac format.

THE BEZZEL INDEX

The Bezzel Index, devised by Bezzel (1980, cited by Stroud *et al.* 1990), has been calculated for Irish breeding bird species and some wintering species to provide some indication of their vulnerability on an international scale. (There are insufficient quantitative data available to apply the Bezzel Index to other vertebrate classes.)

The Index is based on assessments of the area occupied by the species in Europe, their dispersion, population sizes and population trends. It was modified by Stroud *et al.* (1990) to suit conditions in Britain and adapted for this Red Data Book by substituting Irish population statistics. The maximum Bezzel Index is 36, indicating severe vulnerability. In Ireland the Common Scoter has an index of 27 indicating a high level of vulnerability while the Robin has an index of 6, indicating that it is widespread, numerous and generally not vulnerable.

Reservations have been expressed about the value of the Bezzel Index, particularly because it does not give adequate weighting to geographically widespread but declining species (e.g. the Barn Owl; Bezzel Index = 10). However, as the Bezzel Index provides an indication of the vulnerability of many species it was considered worth retaining but no species has been selected using it alone. Further refinements to the Index could be incorporated into future revisions of the Red Data Book.

SPECIES SELECTED

Forty-nine species were selected for inclusion under the various IUCN categories of threat, of which seven are now extinct as breeding species in Ireland. A further nineteen species are included under the Internationally Important category. This produces a total of sixty eight species for inclusion in the Red Data Book, those in the threatened categories making up 21% of all regularly-occurring, extant Irish vertebrates (Table 3 and Appendix III).

In examining candidate species, the criteria have been interpreted broadly so as to include two species that would otherwise have been unjustly left out. The Golden Eagle has been included in the 'Extinct' category even though a pair bred on Fair Head, Antrim, from 1953-60 (i.e. not extinct for 50 years). This species formerly bred widely in Ireland but became extinct as a breeding species in 1912. Similarly, although the Light-bellied Brent Goose is not mentioned in any of the Annexes mentioned in Table 2 it has been included in the 'Internationally Important' category because Ireland is the wintering ground for a large proportion of the sub-population which breeds in Arctic Canada.

TABLE 3 Breakdown of vertebrate classes by Red Data Book category

	Extant Irish species	Extinct	Endangered	Vulnerable	Rare	Indeterminate	RDB Total	% Extant Irish Total	Internationally Important
Mammals	31	1	0	0	1	2	4	13	10
Birds	168	6	8	3	15	3	35	21	7
Reptiles	1	0	0	0	0	0	0	0	0
Amphibians	3	0	1	0	0	0	1	33	1
Fish	27	0	3	3	0	3	9	35	1
Total	230	7	12	6	16	8	49	21	19

GROUPS AND SPECIES EXCLUDED FROM RED DATA BOOK

Introductions

Only species introduced to Ireland prior to 1900 which have become well established and widely distributed have been considered for inclusion in the Red Data Book. Species such as the Rainbow Trout, which was introduced at the beginning of the twentieth century and which bred naturally but never spread, was thus considered but excluded; likewise, the Dace which, although introduced in 1889, has remained confined to one catchment area in the south of Ireland. The Ruddy Duck, which breeds in small numbers in Northern Ireland, is not included in the Red Data Book because it is a feral species.

Subspecies and Morphotypes

Within many vertebrate species there are distinctive subspecies and morphotypes, recognised by their appearance, behaviour, distribution or genetic make up. It is now widely recognised that such genetic variation is worthy of conservation in its own right. However, at the present time there is little genetic information available on Irish vertebrates and it has, therefore, been decided not to include subspecies and morphotypes.

Exceptions have, however, been made for three subspecies which are well recognised and for which Ireland has a special responsibility for their conservation. The Greenland subspecies of the White-fronted Goose and the Light-bellied subspecies of the Brent Goose have been included in the Internationally Important category because a large proportion of the world population of each subspecies winters in Ireland. The Killarney Shad has also been included because it is one of very few landlocked forms of the Twaite Shad.

Bearing in mind the growing need to conserve genetic diversity, serious efforts must be made to identify subspecies and morphotypes in Ireland so that these may be included in revised editions of the Red Data Book if conservation needs dictate.

Wintering Birds

This Red Data Book is concerned primarily with rare or threatened breeding species. It should be noted, however, that several bird species winter or pass through Ireland in very small numbers and could be classified as rare. But, as these species are not threatened in Ireland and are generally common elsewhere in their range, they are not included in the Red Data Book. In a few cases wintering species which are numerous in Ireland but scarce elsewhere have been included in the Internationally Important category.

Intermittent Breeding Birds

A small number of bird species which have, or may have, bred intermittently (fewer than 3 records) or in very small numbers since 1970 and have no history of previous breeding have been excluded from the Red Data Book, although they could be included in future editions. These include Black-throated Diver, Montagu's Harrier, Osprey, Dotterel, Savi's Warbler, Lesser Whitethroat and Hawfinch (Appendix IV). A number of other species have been occurring in Ireland with increasing frequency and seem likely to become established as breeding species within the next few years, including Goshawk and Hobby.

Scarce Breeding Birds which are not Threatened in Ireland

Included among the Irish avifauna are a number of birds which are common breeding species in Britain and continental Europe but are scarce breeders in Ireland. These are species whose scarcity in Ireland is probably due to the absence of suitable habitats or climatic barriers and in many cases are 'edge-of-range' species. Examples include: Quail, Turtle Dove, Tree Pipit, Yellow Wagtail, Redstart, Reed Warbler, Garden Warbler and Pied Flycatcher. In Ireland these species utilise a variety of breeding habitats none of which is considered particularly threatened though several may be limited in extent (e.g. woodlands for Pied Flycatcher and Redstart). Further information is required to confirm the status of these species and their habitats, so, for the time being, they have been excluded from the Red Data Book.

A few edge-of-range species are included where a threat has been identified. Examples include: Bearded Tit, threatened by reedbed destruction in coastal lagoons, and Wood Warbler whose preferred habitat - oakwoods with little secondary growth and sparse vegetation cover - is vulnerable.

POPULATION TRENDS IN RED DATA BOOK SPECIES

Generally, there are insufficient data available to establish population trends for most of the Red Data Book species. Satisfactory quantitative data are available for only a small proportion of the total Irish vertebrate fauna of 230 species.

The downward trend in the numbers of breeding Common Scoters on Lough Erne is well documented and probably reflects the general trend for the species. Likewise, it is clear from field records that the Corncrake and the Red-necked Phalarope have declined in numbers over several decades whilst the Irish Roseate Tern population has recently stabilised somewhat following a dramatic decline. The Little Tern population may be reasonably stable, but there are no satisfactory quantitative data from the west coast to substantiate this suggestion. The Whooper Swan, Greenland White-fronted Goose, Brent Goose and Peregrine Falcon have increased in numbers during the last two decades and Chough numbers seem to be stable. The Otter population may also be fairly stable but little is known of the population trends of other Irish mammals, amphibians, fish or the single reptile, the Viviparous Lizard. Therefore, we are not in a position to judge in any quantitative way how most Irish vertebrate populations are changing.

FUTURE REVIEW / NEAR-THREATENED SPECIES

This Red Data Book, like all others, is not the last word on rare and endangered species. It is intended primarily to be a working document for those who must make decisions on and actively undertake the conservation of

Irish wildlife. It is not written in stone, as a commandment for all time. A Red Data Book must be flexible. It is a starting point and must be updated and revised at regular intervals if it is to serve its purpose effectively. If rare or threatened species become more abundant or escape from beneath the cloud of threat, they can be dropped from the Red Data Book. On the other hand, species can be added if concern arises about their survival. Species can, of course, also be shifted from category to category within the Red Data Book as circumstances dictate.

Several species which still have relatively large populations in Ireland are declining or could easily come under pressure from further habitat loss or deterioration. Examples are birds such as the Red Grouse, Curlew, Ringed Plover, Redshank, Common Sandpiper, Razorbill, Puffin, Cuckoo, Kingfisher, Dipper, Redstart and fish such as the Brown Trout, Rudd and Nine-spined Stickleback. Although these species (which might be termed 'Near-threatened') do not yet warrant inclusion as threatened species in the Red Data Book they need to be closely monitored to ascertain their status so that consideration may be given to their inclusion in future editions of the Red Data Book.

3 TAXONOMIC LIST OF RED DATA BOOK SPECIES

The nomenclature and order follows that given by Corbet and Harris (1991) for mammals, Voous (1977) for birds, Frazer (1983) for amphibians, and Maitland and Campbell (1992) for fish.

MAMMALS

		RDB Category
Threatened or Extinct		
Whiskered Bat	*Myotis mystacinus* (Kuhl)	I
Natterer's Bat	*Myotis nattereri* (Kuhl)	I
Ship Rat	*Rattus rattus* (L.)	R
Grey Wolf	*Canis lupus* L.	Ex
Internationally Important		
Hedgehog	*Erinaceus europaeus* L.	II
Lesser Horseshoe Bat	*Rhinolophus hipposideros* (Bechstein)	II
Daubenton's Bat	*Myotis daubentoni* (Kuhl)	II
Leisler's Bat	*Nyctalus leisleri* (Kuhl)	II
Pipistrelle	*Pipistrellus pipistrellus* (Schreber)	II
Brown Long-eared Bat	*Plecotus auritus* (L.)	II
Irish Hare	*Lepus timidus hibernicus* L.	II
Pine Marten	*Martes martes* (L.)	II
Badger	*Meles meles* (L.)	II
Otter	*Lutra lutra* (L.)	II

BIRDS

Threatened or Extinct		
Red-throated Diver	*Gavia stellata* (Pontoppidan)	R
Black-necked Grebe	*Podiceps nigricollis* Brehm	R
Bittern	*Botaurus stellaris* (L.)	Ex
Gadwall	*Anas strepera* L.	R
Pintail	*Anas acuta* L.	R
Garganey	*Anas querquedula* L.	R
Shoveler	*Anas clypeata* L.	R
Pochard	*Aythya ferina* (L.)	R
Common Scoter	*Melanitta nigra* (L.)	E
Goosander	*Mergus merganser* L.	R
White-tailed Eagle	*Haliaeetus albicilla* (L.)	Ex
Marsh Harrier	*Circus aeruginosus* (L.)	Ex
Hen Harrier	*Circus cyaneus* (L.)	E
Golden Eagle	*Aquila chrysaetos* (L.)	Ex
Merlin	*Falco columbarius* L.	R
Capercaillie	*Tetrao urogallus* L.	Ex
Grey Partridge	*Perdix perdix* (L.)	E
Corncrake	*Crex crex* (L.)	E
Golden Plover	*Pluvialis apricaria* (L.)	V
Dunlin	*Calidris alpina* (L.)	V
Black-tailed Godwit	*Limosa limosa* (L.)	R

Greenshank	*Tringa nebularia* (Gunnerus)	R
Red-necked Phalarope	*Phalaropus lobatus* (L.)	E
Roseate Tern	*Sterna dougallii* Montagu	E
Little Tern	*Sterna albifrons* Pallas	V
Barn Owl	*Tyto alba* (Scopoli)	I
Short-eared Owl	*Asio flammeus* (Pontoppidan)	R
Nightjar	*Caprimulgus europaeus* L.	E
Woodlark	*Lullula arborea* (L.)	Ex
Ring Ouzel	*Turdus torquatus* L.	R
Wood Warbler	*Phylloscopus sibilatrix* (Bechstein)	R
Bearded Tit	*Panurus biarmicus* (L.)	R
Tree Sparrow	*Passer montanus* (L.)	I
Twite	*Carduelis flavirostris* (L.)	I
Corn Bunting	*Miliaria calandra* L.	E
Internationally Important		
Storm Petrel	*Hydrobates pelagicus* (L.)	II
Whooper Swan	*Cygnus cygnus* (L.)	II
Greenland White-fronted Goose	*Anser albifrons flavirostris* Dalgety and Scott	II
Barnacle Goose	*Branta leucopsis* (Bechstein)	II
Light-bellied Brent Goose	*Branta bernicla hrota* (Müller)	II
Peregrine	*Falco peregrinus* Tunstall	II
Chough	*Pyrrhocorax pyrrhocorax* (L.)	II

AMPHIBIANS

Threatened

Natterjack Toad	*Bufo calamita* Laurenti	E
Internationally Important		
Common Frog	*Rana temporaria* L.	II

FISH

Threatened

Sea Lamprey	*Petromyzon marinus* L.	I
River Lamprey	*Lampetra fluviatilis* (L.)	I
Brook Lamprey	*Lampetra planeri* (Bloch)	I
Allis Shad	*Alosa alosa* (L.)	E
Twaite Shad	*Alosa fallax fallax* (Lacépède)	V
Killarney Shad	*Alosa fallax killarnensis* Regan.	E
Arctic Charr	*Salvelinus alpinus* (L.)	V
Pollan	*Coregonus autumnalis pollan* Thompson	E
Smelt	*Osmerus eperlanus* (L.)	V
Internationally Important		
Atlantic Salmon	*Salmo salar* L.	II

Key

Ex Extinct
E Endangered
V Vulnerable
R Rare
I Indeterminate
II Internationally Important

4 THE SPECIES ACCOUNTS

INTRODUCTION TO THE SPECIES ACCOUNTS

The Red Data species accounts are presented in taxonomic order beginning with mammals, followed by birds, amphibians and fish. Within each class, threatened and extinct species receive a full account and are presented first, followed by a summary account of the internationally important species which are not considered threatened in Ireland.

Each account is divided into five sections. Below the species heading and IUCN category are five paragraphs: an introduction, providing a brief outline of the natural history of the species, the history of the species in Ireland, current distribution and status, threats, and finally conservation - in progress or required. In addition, there is a boxed summary of the status of the species under Irish and European legislation and information on its numbers, occurrence in Ireland and main food.

Preparation of the data sheets has taken account of data available up to September 1992 with some supplementary information added up to October 1993.

EXPLANATION OF ABBREVIATIONS USED IN SUMMARY BOX

The symbols and abbreviations used in the Summary Box of the Species Accounts are explained below.

LEG STATUS IRL

The legal status of the species under wildlife legislation in the Republic of Ireland (RoI) and Northern Ireland (NI)(Appendix V).

Protected = species protected at all times under the Wildlife (Northern Ireland) Order 1985 and/or under the Wildlife Act (1976) in the Republic of Ireland.

Unprotected = species not explicitly protected under the law.

Quarry = species which may be hunted for periods of the year as specified under the Wildlife Order and the Open Seasons Order of the Wildlife Act (1976).

Commercial = fish species that are caught commercially.

LEG STATUS EUR

The legal status of the species under European legislation (EC directives and international conventions). See Appendix V for fuller description.

Birds Dir = EC Directive on the Conservation of Wild Birds (79/409/EEC) commonly known as the 'Birds Directive'
Annex I: Species whose status is a cause of concern and require special conservation measures.
Annex II: Quarry species
Annex III: Quarry species that may be sold

Habitats Dir = EC Directive on the Conservation of Natural Habitats and of Wild Fauna and Flora (92/43/EEC) commonly known as the 'Habitats Directive'
Annex II: Species requiring the designation of Special Areas of Conservation
Annex IV: Species in need of strict protection
Annex V: Species which may be subject to management measures

Bern = The Convention on the Conservation of European Wildlife and Natural Habitats (1979) commonly known as the 'Bern Convention'
Appendix II: Strictly protected fauna species
Appendix III: Protected fauna species

Bonn = The Convention on the Conservation of Migratory Species of Wild Animals (1979) commonly known as the 'Bonn Convention'
Appendix I: Endangered migratory species
Appendix II: Migratory species requiring conservation

INTL LEG STATUS

The legal status of the species under international law. Listing in IUCN Red List of Threatened Animals (IUCN 1990) or listing in the UN's European Red List (United Nations 1991).

IUCN Red List 1990
V = Vulnerable on a world scale
R = Rare on a world scale

UN European Red List 1991
Categories as per IUCN List; some extra species included.

BEZZEL INDEX, IRELAND

Calculated for birds only (see page 7)

B = Breeding
W = Wintering

OCCURRENCE IN IRELAND

The status of the species in Ireland (birds only)

R = Resident

S = Summer visitor (breeding)

P = Passage migrant

W = Winter visitor

[ ] = Intermittent

BREEDING PAIRS

The most recent estimate of the numbers of breeding pairs in Ireland (birds only).

WINTERING OR PASSAGE NUMBERS

The most recent estimate of numbers wintering or on passage in Ireland (birds only).

NUMBERS

The most recent estimates of numbers in Ireland (other groups).

MAIN FOOD

Indication of the main foods taken by the species.

MIGRATORY STATUS (FISH ONLY)

Anadromous -migrates from sea to freshwater to breed

Non-migratory-spends whole life-cycle in freshwater

MAMMALS

MAMMALS

Common Name	Scientific Name	RDB Category	Page
Species Threatened or Extinct in Ireland			
Whiskered Bat	*Myotis mystacinus*	I	20
Natterer's Bat	*Myotis nattereri*	I	23
Ship Rat	*Rattus rattus*	R	26
Grey Wolf	*Canis lupus*	Ex	28
Internationally Important Species			
Hedgehog	*Erinaceus europaeus*	II	30
Lesser-horseshoe Bat	*Rhinolophus hipposideros*	II	30
Daubenton's Bat	*Myotis daubentoni*	II	31
Leisler's Bat	*Nyctalus leisleri*	II	31
Pipistrelle	*Pistrellus pipistrellus*	II	32
Brown Long-eared Bat	*Plecotus auritus*	II	32
Irish Hare	*Lepus timidus hibernicus*	II	33
Pine Marten	*Martes martes*	II	33
Badger	*Meles meles*	II	34
Otter	*Lutra lutra*	II	34

Key
Ex Extinct
E Endangered
V Vulnerable
R Rare
I Indeterminate
II Internationally Important

WHISKERED BAT

Myotis mystacinus

Indeterminate

R.E. Stebbings

The Whiskered Bat is a widely distributed but infrequently recorded species. In summer it roosts in houses and is usually found in roofs between rafters or in narrow slits where the timbers meet. It feeds in wooded, open country and riparian habitats picking small insects and spiders off foliage (O'Sullivan in press). In winter it roosts in hollow trees, caves, mines, cellars and under bridges. Its small numbers may be attributed to the fact that in Ireland it is at the north-western edge of its range.

LEG STATUS IRL	RoI Protected	LEG STATUS EUR	Habitats Dir	IV
	NI Protected		Bern	II
INTL LEG STATUS			Bonn	–
NUMBERS	Few (hundreds?)			
MAIN FOOD	Small insects and spiders			

History of the Species in Ireland

The Whiskered Bat was first recorded in Clare in 1852 (Fairley 1984) and then in 1896 after which its range was reported to extend to Wexford, Carlow,

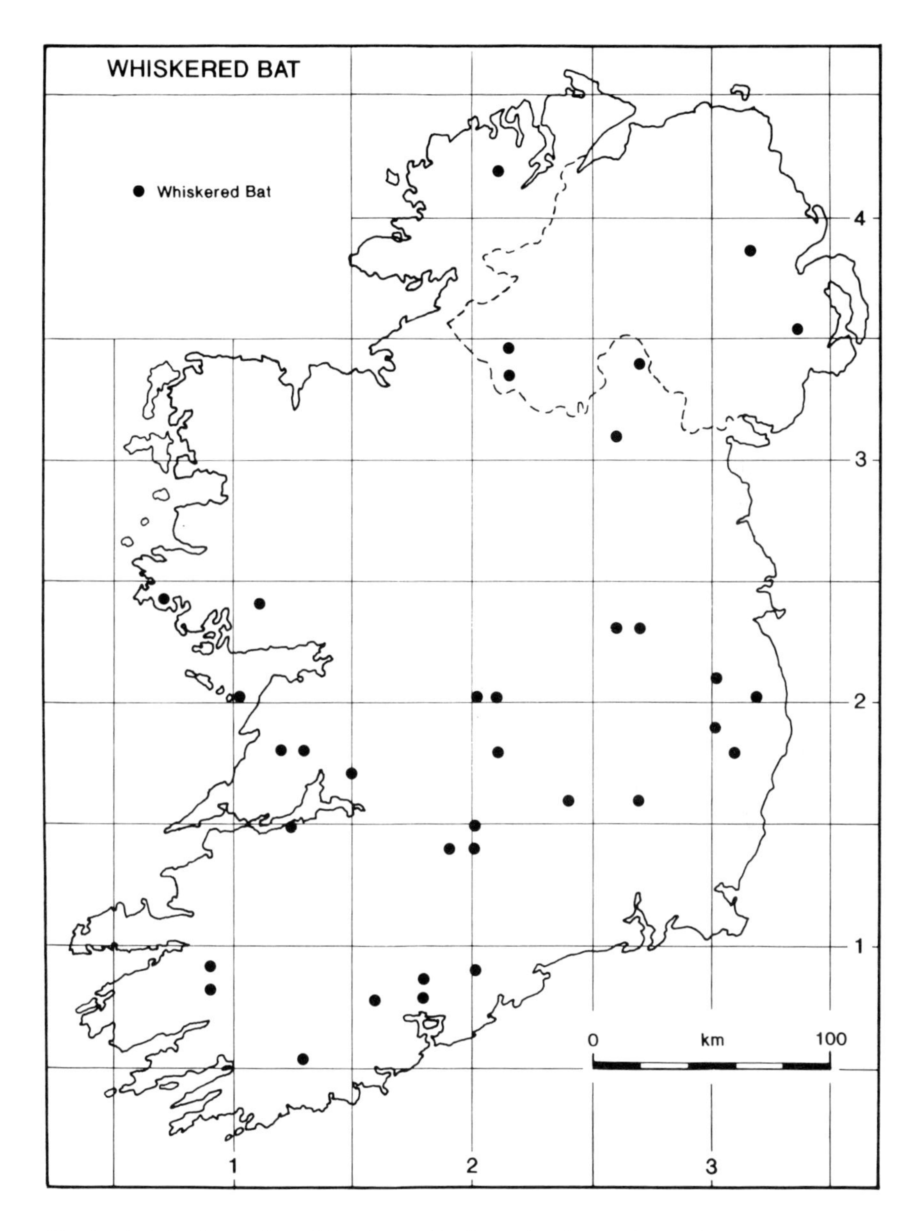

Fig 1 Distribution of the Whiskered Bat in Ireland based on 10 km squares (Source: National Parks and Wildlife Service and Northern Ireland Bat Group)

Dublin, Louth, Fermanagh and Down, though Moffat (1938) believed that it probably occurred in most counties in the early part of the century (O'Rourke 1970). Between 1910 and 1980 there was only one report of the species (O'Sullivan in press).

Current Distribution and Status

The Whiskered Bat occurs throughout Europe – except in Iceland, northern Fenno-Scandia, Denmark, Scotland, southern France and much of Spain and Portugal – and eastwards through central Asia, possibly through China to Japan (Corbet and Harris 1991). There are only scattered records from its European range where it forms small, dispersed colonies and is considered to be rare and vulnerable throughout. Some populations are known to have declined but others are possibly increasing slightly (Stebbings and Griffith 1986).

In Britain, where it is classed as 'vulnerable' (Whitten 1990), it probably occurs throughout England and Wales and in south-west Wales it is one of the most abundant species which forms nursery colonies in buildings (Stebbings and Griffith 1986).

Nothing is known about its status elsewhere in the world (Stebbings and Griffith 1986).

In the 1985–1988 survey in the Republic it was recorded at only 34 roosts (Figure 1), most of which contained only one to ten bats. Most roosts had less than five bats and only six had more than ten making it the rarest bat species in Ireland – though the Irish population is still likely to be significant in a European context. It has been recorded in Antrim (1), Down (1), Fermanagh (2) (Northern Ireland Bat Group), Donegal (1), Monaghan (1), Galway (6), Clare (5), Wicklow (6), Carlow (1), Kilkenny (1), Offaly (1), Tipperary (6), Kerry (2), Cork (7) and Waterford (1) (O'Sullivan in press; McAney 1987; Fairley 1991; Smiddy 1991). (Bracketed numbers indicate number of roosts recorded to date.) This distribution, however, is perhaps more representative of the distribution of observers than of bats and the species may occur throughout the country. The small number of tiny colonies recorded suggests that the total population may be in the low hundreds.

It is the only species recorded by O'Sullivan (in press) roosting with other species of bats – Lesser Horseshoe, Natterer's, Pipistrelle and Brown Long-eared.

Threats

Remedial timber treatment, the pointing of bridges, disturbance and other actions taken as a result of the 'unfavourable public image' of bats in general appear to be the main threats to the Whiskered Bat. The use of insecticides and pesticides and agricultural intensification may be reducing prey abundance for bats generally.

Conservation

Further survey work will be needed to determine the true size and distribution of the population and it will be necessary to protect the major colonies. Measures to control the pointing of bridges used by bats will be required in the Republic to match those in effect in Northern Ireland. Education is needed to combat an unfavourable public image.

NATTERER'S BAT

Myotis nattereri **Indeterminate**

R.E. Stebbings

In summer Natterer's Bat roosts and breeds in buildings and in winter it roosts in caves and tunnels. It hides in cracks and crevices and can be very difficult to find when numbers are low. It feeds on large insects and other arthropods (Shiel *et al.* 1991), sometimes taking them from foliage, from the ground and along woodland edges (O'Sullivan in press), often close to water. Apart from the fact that in Ireland it is at the north-western edge of its range there are no apparent reasons for its low numbers (P. O'Sullivan).

LEG STATUS IRL	RoI Protected	**LEG STATUS EUR**	Habitats Dir	IV
	NI Protected		Bern	II
INTL LEG STATUS	UN I		Bonn	–
NUMBERS	Unknown (c 1,000?)			
MAIN FOOD	Large insects and other arthropods			

History of the Species in Ireland

Natterer's Bat was found in Neolithic strata in Britain (Corbet and Harris 1991) so it may also have been present in Ireland in late post-glacial times. In

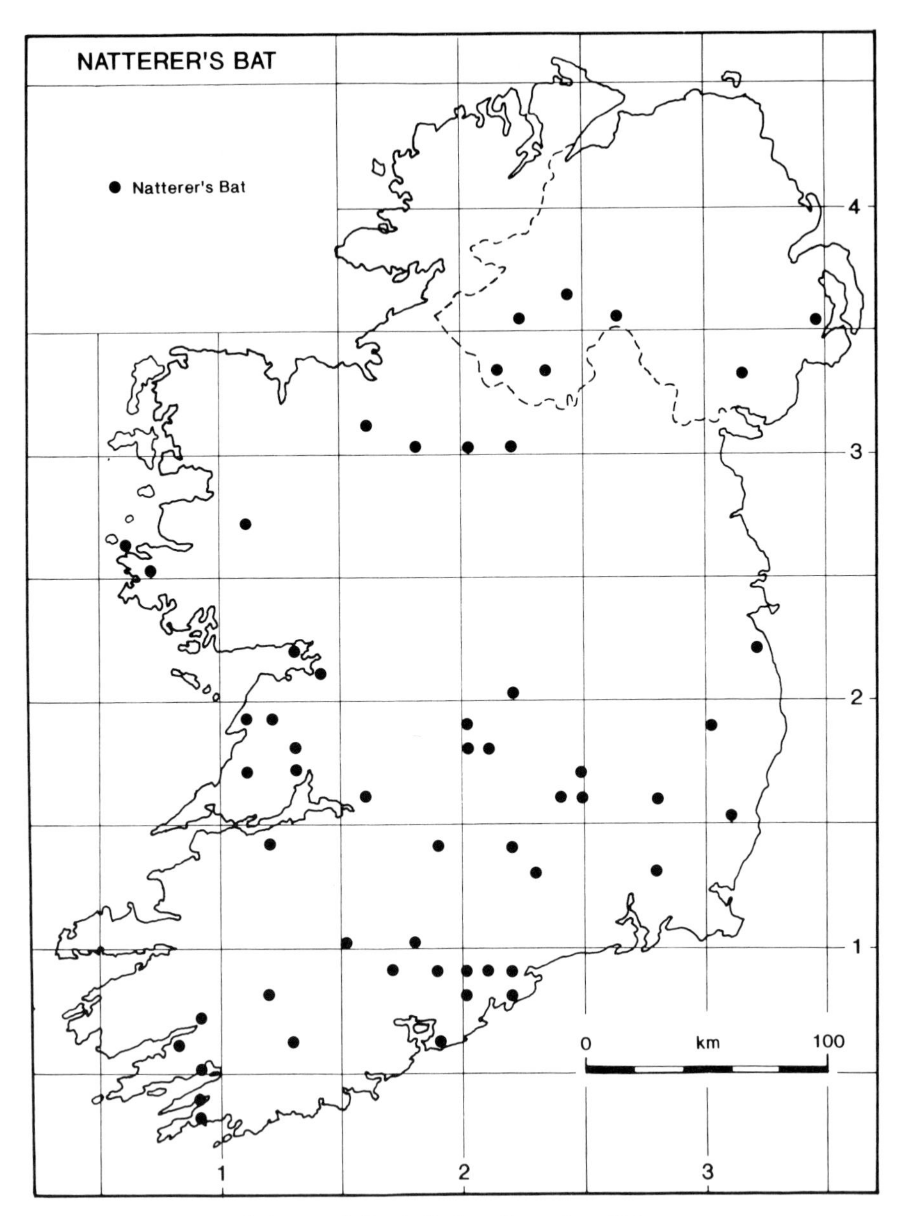

Fig 2 Distribution of Natterer's Bat in Ireland based on 10 km squares (Source: National Parks and Wildlife Service and Northern Ireland Bat Group)

the early part of the twentieth century it was recorded in eleven counties (Moffat 1938) but since then few records have been produced.

Current Distribution and Status

Natterer's Bat occurs throughout Europe – except in Iceland and northern Fenno-Scandia – and eastwards to the Caucasus, with outlying populations in North Africa, southern and central Asia and China. It is known to have declined in some areas and is considered to be vulnerable in the EC but little is known about its status.

In Britain, where it is classed as 'Vulnerable' (Whitten 1990), it is widespread but more common in the south. Nothing is known of its status elsewhere in the world. (Stebbings and Griffith 1986).

In the 1985–88 survey 44 roosts were located in the Republic and of these twenty held single bats while only seven held over fifty bats. It has been recorded in Down (2), Tyrone (2), Fermanagh (3) (Northern Ireland Bat Group) and in Sligo, Leitrim, Cavan, Monaghan, Roscommon, Mayo, Galway, Offaly, Laois, Carlow, Wexford, Tipperary, Clare, Limerick, Kerry, Cork and Waterford (O'Sullivan in press; Smiddy 1987, 1991) (Figure 2) (Bracketed numbers indicate number of roosts recorded to date.). The small number of relatively small roosts suggests that the population in the Republic may be around 1,000, or in the low thousands at most, and in Northern Ireland less than 200 (P. Allen).

Threats

The main threats to this species are habitat destruction, remedial timber treatment, disturbance and other actions taken as a result of the 'unfavourable public image' shared with all bats. The use of insecticides and pesticides and agricultural intensification may be reducing prey abundance for bats generally.

Conservation

Population surveys have been conducted in Northern Ireland and in the Republic. However, these will need to be extended and intensified if the true status of the species is to be determined. There is a need to protect major colonies and the habitats used by the bats and to improve its public image through education and publicity.

SHIP RAT

Rattus rattus **Rare**

R.T. Mills

The Ship Rat, also known as the Black Rat, is similar in appearance to the Common Rat but has relatively larger eyes and ears and a longer, thinner, unicoloured tail (Corbet and Harris 1991). Currently it is known to occur on one offshore island and it may also inhabit buildings at a small number of mainland coastal locations. Its limited distribution and small numbers result from competition with the Common Rat and human persecution.

LEG STATUS IRL	RoI Unprotected	**LEG STATUS EUR**	Habitats Dir	–
	NI Unprotected		Bern	–
INTL LEG STATUS			Bonn	–
NUMBERS	Unknown			
MAIN FOOD	Cereals and other plant material, occasionally animal material			

History of the Species in Ireland

The Ship Rat was reported by Giraldus Cambrensis to be in Ireland in 1185 (Fairley 1984) but it is likely to have been present for a considerable time prior to that (Corbet and Harris 1991). It was probably widespread in human habitation until it was rapidly replaced by the Common Rat which was introduced in the early 1700s.

A colony may have existed on Lambay Island off Dublin in the 1930s (Moffat 1938) and the species was recorded co-existing with the Common Rat on Lambay in 1985 (Walsh 1988). The species was also reported inland in Lurgan in Armagh and Tyrella in Down (Deane 1952), in ports in Londonderry in 1951 and in Belfast in 1951 to 1961 (Bentley 1959, 1964), in Dublin and in the vicinity of Newry, Waterford and Cork since 1950 and near Dungarvan before 1950 (Ni Lamhna 1979).

Current Distribution and Status

The Ship Rat occurs in urban areas throughout the tropics and subtropics, extending to many small villages and even remote farms, but does not live away from buildings except on islands where there are few or no indigenous competitors. It is widespread throughout the EC and elsewhere in continental Europe and is a serious pest in plantations in the Mediterranean area (Macdonald and Barrett 1993).

Formerly it was widespread in Britain but is now found only in London dockland and on Lundy Island (Macdonald and Barrett, 1993), where it apparently co-exists with the Common Rat (Smith 1991).

In Ireland the only recent record was that from Lambay (Walsh 1988).

Threats

Deliberate extermination and competition with the Common Rat, which is more aggressive.

Conservation

No conservation action has been taken and none is envisaged as this species is considered to be a potential public health hazard.

GREY WOLF

Canis lupus

Extinct

Heather Angel

The Grey Wolf has been extinct in Ireland since the late eighteenth century following centuries of persecution by man. Relict populations still remain in a few EC countries. While some of these are given legal protection, often this is only minimally enforced, if at all. Where healthy Wolf populations still survive they occupy a variety of habitats including tundra, forest, open plains and desert margins. Wolves take a wide range of mammalian prey. Where natural prey has been reduced they will take almost any kind of domestic animal (WCMC 1989).

LEG STATUS IRL	RoI –	**LEG STATUS EUR**	Habitats Dir	II,IV,V
	NI –		Bern	II
INTL LEG STATUS	UN V, IUCN V		Bonn	–
NUMBERS	–			

MAIN FOOD Large and medium-sized mammals; domestic animals

History of the Species in Ireland

The Grey Wolf was present in Ireland during the late Pleistocene (18,000–40,000 years ago) but unlike many of the other mammals (Woolly

Mammoth, Brown Bear, Spotted Hyaena, Arctic Fox, Irish Giant Deer, Reindeer, Horse, Norwegian Lemming and Greenland Lemming; Mitchell 1976) it survived into historic times.

In the past, Wolves were despised in Ireland because of their reported attacks on man and their depredations of domestic animals. Wolves were still plentiful in 1600 but thereafter, during the Plantation of Ireland, a sustained campaign of eradication rapidly led to their demise (Fairley 1984). Habitat loss, through woodland clearance, also played a large part in the extermination.

From 1683 onwards the paucity of Wolves is mentioned more and more frequently. There is much debate about where and when the last Irish Grey Wolf was killed. The most widely quoted date is 1786 at Ballydarton, Co Carlow, but Fairley (1984) argues that no satisfactory authenticated report on this subject exists.

Current Distribution and Status

The original range of the Grey Wolf was very large, covering Europe, Northern Asia and North America. The Wolf is now extinct throughout most of Western Europe with small relict populations (numbers in brackets) left in: Albania, Bulgaria (100), Czechoslovakia (<100), Finland (100), Greece (>500), Italy (>150), Norway (6), Poland (880), Portugal (200), Spain (<200), Sweden (a few), Turkey, and former Yugoslavia (>2,000). The Wolf has an extensive but patchy distribution in European Russia. Based on the above figures the population estimate for the EC in the mid 1980s was over 1,000 animals (WCMC 1989).

Threats

The Grey Wolf has now been exterminated over much of its range and seriously depleted in the remainder. The main reasons for the decline are habitat loss to human settlement and agriculture, and intense persecution by man. Where it still survives in the EC it is threatened by continuing habitat loss, prey extermination, hunting, and competition/hybridization with stray and feral dogs. In Spain Wolves are hunted for sport.

Conservation

No measures required.

HEDGEHOG

Erinaceus europaeus — **Internationally Important**

It is considered that the Hedgehog is widespread and common in Ireland but threatened in Europe (Rudge 1984). While Ni Lamhna (1979) provides a distribution map there is a need for up-to-date data on the Hedgehog in Ireland and a comprehensive survey is required.

LEG STATUS IRL	RoI Protected	**LEG STATUS EUR**	Habitats Dir	–
	NI Unprotected*		Bern	III
INTL LEG STATUS			Bonn	–
NUMBERS	Unknown			
MAIN FOOD	Ground-dwelling invertebrates			

* But may not be sold alive or dead at any time

LESSER HORSESHOE BAT

Rhinolophus hipposideros — **Internationally Important**

This species is the smallest European horseshoe bat and one of the most sensitive to disturbance. Ireland has the largest national population of Lesser Horseshoe Bats in Europe and it has been recorded in 157 roosts in the Republic to date (O'Sullivan in press). It is confined to the west and south-west and has not been recorded in Northern Ireland. The loss of suitable summer sites and disturbance during hibernation are the major threats facing this species.

LEG STATUS IRL	RoI Protected	**LEG STATUS EUR**	Habitats Dir	II/IV
	NI Protected		Bern	II
INTL LEG STATUS			Bonn	–
NUMBERS	c 12,000			
MAIN FOOD	Insects and spiders			

DAUBENTON'S BAT

Myotis daubentoni **Internationally Important**

Daubenton's Bat is widespread and probably under-recorded. To date it has been recorded in over 200 roosts in the Republic (O'Sullivan in press; Smiddy 1991) but at only five in Northern Ireland where it may have been under-recorded (P. Allen). It is threatened in some localities by the pointing and re-inforcing of bridges (O'Sullivan in press). In Europe, and on a world-wide scale, it is not clear whether it is threatened (Stebbings and Griffith 1986).

LEG STATUS IRL	RoI Protected	LEG STATUS EUR	Habitats Dir IV
	NI Protected		Bern II
INTL LEG STATUS			Bonn –
NUMBERS	Unknown (low thousands?)		
MAIN FOOD	Insects		

LEISLER'S BAT

Nyctalus leisleri **Internationally Important**

Ireland, at the northern edge of its range, is the major stronghold in Europe for Leisler's Bat. It is considered to be rare and possibly vulnerable elsewhere in Europe and vulnerable in a world context (Stebbings and Griffith 1986). It is widespread and numerous in Ireland and has been recorded in 108 roosts to date. Large roosts of at least 500 individuals have been recorded in buildings in the west of Ireland (McAney and Fairley 1990). It may be abundant in Ireland because the larger congener, the Noctule is absent (J.S. Fairley). Exclusion from roosts is the main threat facing this species.

LEG STATUS IRL	RoI Protected	LEG STATUS EUR	Habitats Dir IV
	NI Protected		Bern II
INTL LEG STATUS			Bonn –
NUMBERS	Unknown (several thousands?)		
MAIN FOOD	Insects		

PIPISTRELLE

Pipistrellus pipistrellus — **Internationally Important**

The Pipistrelle is Ireland's most widespread and numerous bat and has been recorded at 748 roosts to date. Nursery roosts containing over 500 individuals are often recorded. It is also widespread and common elsewhere in Europe but considered to be vulnerable there and throughout the rest of its world range (Stebbings and Griffith 1986). Exclusion from roosts is the main threat facing the Pipistrelle in Ireland.

LEG STATUS IRL	RoI Protected	**LEG STATUS EUR**	Habitats Dir	IV
	NI Protected		Bern	III
INTL LEG STATUS			Bonn	–
NUMBERS	Unknown			
MAIN FOOD Insects				

BROWN LONG-EARED BAT

Plecotus auritus — **Internationally Important**

The Brown Long-eared Bat is the second most frequently recorded bat in Ireland with over 340 roosts reported to date (P. O'Sullivan in press; Smiddy 1991). It occurs throughout mainland Ireland and on off-shore islands. It is also widespread and common elsewhere in Europe but is considered to be vulnerable there as elsewhere in its world range (Stebbings and Griffith 1986). The majority of roosts are small, consisting of fewer than 50 individuals.

LEG STATUS IRL	RoI Protected	**LEG STATUS EUR**	Habitats Dir	IV
	NI Protected		Bern	II
INTL LEG STATUS	UN I		Bonn	–
NUMBERS	Unknown			
MAIN FOOD Insects (flying and non-flying) and spiders				

IRISH HARE

Lepus timidus hibernicus **Internationally Important**

The Irish (or Mountain) Hare is considered to be widespread and common in Ireland. Elsewhere in Europe it is common in Scotland and Fenno-Scandia but considered to be threatened in the rest of its range in the alpine regions of Germany, Italy and France (Rudge 1984). The Irish sub-species *Lepus timidus hibernicus* is distinct in its feeding ecology and habitat requirements and local adaptation is evident from its capacity to eat grasses and retain a brown winter coat in a generally snowless environment (R. Harrington).

LEG STATUS IRL	RoI	Quarry	**LEG STATUS EUR**	Habitats Dir	V
	NI	Quarry		Bern	III
INTL LEG STATUS				Bonn	–
NUMBERS		Unknown			
MAIN FOOD	Heather, grasses, sedges and crops				

PINE MARTEN

Martes martes **Internationally Important**

Although the Pine Marten is widespread only in the west of Ireland, its numbers are increasing and it is expanding its range (O'Sullivan 1983; P. O'Sullivan) and is considered to be secure, particularly now that the laying of strychnine has been banned. It is considered to be threatened in seven out of the other nine EC countries in which it occurs (Rudge 1984).

LEG STATUS IRL	RoI	Protected	**LEG STATUS EUR**	Habitats Dir	V
	NI	Protected		Bern	III
INTL LEG STATUS				Bonn	–
NUMBERS		Unknown			
MAIN FOOD	Small vertebrates, beetles and other invertebrates, and berries				

BADGER

Meles meles

Internationally Important

The Badger is common and widespread in Ireland. The population has been surveyed in Northern Ireland and is currently being surveyed in the Republic (Smal 1991). Although implicated in the transmission of bovine tuberculosis and persecuted in some areas there is little reason to believe that the Badger is in any way threatened overall. However, in Europe it is considered that it may be vulnerable in parts of its range (Rudge 1984).

LEG STATUS IRL	RoI Protected	**LEG STATUS EUR**	Habitats Dir	–
	NI Protected		Bern	III
INTL LEG STATUS			Bonn	–
NUMBERS	c 250,000 adults (Smal 1991)			
MAIN FOOD	Wide range of animal and plant material			

OTTER

Lutra lutra

Internationally Important

Ireland has the densest population of Otters in western Europe. They occur throughout the country in freshwater and coastal habitats (Chapman and Chapman 1982) and there appears to have been little change in status since 1981 according to the preliminary results of a repeat survey of sample sites in 1990 (Lunnan and Reynolds 1991). Elsewhere in Europe it is thinly distributed or extinct (e.g. in the Netherlands) (Rudge 1984). It is considered to be sparsely distributed or extinct in large parts of its original range and is classified as "vulnerable" on a worldwide scale by the IUCN (1990).

LEG STATUS IRL	RoI Protected	**LEG STATUS EUR**	Habitats Dir	II/IV
	NI Protected		Bern	II
INTL LEG STATUS	IUCN V		Bonn	–
NUMBERS	Several thousands?			
MAIN FOOD	Fish			

BIRDS

BIRDS

Common Name	Scientific Name	RDB Category	Page
Species Threatened or Extinct in Ireland			
Red-throated Diver	*Gavia stellata*	R	39
Black-necked Grebe	*Podiceps nigricollis*	R	42
Bittern	*Botaurus stellaris*	Ex	44
Gadwall	*Anas strepera*	R	47
Pintail	*Anas acuta*	R	50
Garganey	*Anas querquedula*	R	52
Shoveler	*Anas clypeata*	R	54
Pochard	*Aythya ferina*	R	56
Common Scoter	*Melanitta nigra*	E	58
Goosander	*Mergus merganser*	R	62
White-tailed Eagle	*Haliaeetus albicilla*	Ex	64
Marsh Harrier	*Circus aeruginosus*	Ex	67
Hen Harrier	*Circus cyaneus*	E	69
Golden Eagle	*Aquila chrysaetos*	Ex	72
Merlin	*Falco columbarius*	R	74
Capercaillie	*Tetrao urogallus*	Ex	77
Grey Partridge	*Perdix perdix*	E	79
Corncrake	*Crex crex*	E	82
Golden Plover	*Pluvialis apricaria*	V	86
Dunlin	*Calidris alpina*	V	89
Black-tailed Godwit	*Limosa limosa*	R	91
Greenshank	*Tringa nebularia*	R	93
Red-necked Phalarope	*Phalaropus lobatus*	E	95
Roseate Tern	*Sterna dougallii*	E	98
Little Tern	*Sterna albifrons*	V	103
Barn Owl	*Tyto alba*	I	106
Short-eared Owl	*Asio flammeus*	R	110
Nightjar	*Caprimulgus europaeus*	E	112
Woodlark	*Lullula arborea*	Ex	115
Ring Ouzel	*Turdus torquatus*	R	117
Wood Warbler	*Phylloscopus sibilatrix*	R	119
Bearded Tit	*Panurus biarmicus*	R	121
Tree Sparrow	*Passer montanus*	I	123
Twite	*Carduelis flavirostris*	I	126
Corn Bunting	*Miliaria calandra*	E	129
Internationally Important Species			
Storm Petrel	*Hydrobates pelagicus*	II	131
Whooper Swan	*Cygnus cygnus*	II	131

Common Name	Scientific Name	RDB Category	Page
Internationally Important Species (continued)			
Greenland White-fronted Goose	*Anser albifrons flavirostris*	II	132
Barnacle Goose	*Branta leucopsis*	II	132
Light-bellied Brent Goose	*Branta bernicla hrota*	II	133
Peregrine	*Falco peregrinus*	II	133
Chough	*Pyrrhocorax pyrrhocorax*	II	134

Key

Ex Extinct
E Endangered
V Vulnerable
R Rare
I Indeterminate
II Internationally Important

SPECIES THREATENED OR EXTINCT IN IRELAND

RED-THROATED DIVER

Gavia stellata **Rare**

INP/J. Malins

The Red-throated Diver is a rare breeding species in Ireland, being confined, as far as is known, to small mountain loughs in Donegal. In winter it occurs widely around the coast but in small numbers. Its scarcity as a breeding bird can be attributed to the fact that in Ireland it is breeding at the southern edge of its range.

LEG STATUS IRL	RoI Protected	**LEG STATUS EUR**	Birds Dir	I
	NI Protected		Bern	II
INTL LEG STATUS			Bonn	–
OCCURRENCE IN IRELAND	S,W,P	**BEZZEL INDEX, IRELAND**		18
BREEDING PAIRS	Unknown (<10)	**WINTERING NUMBERS**		200–500
MAIN FOOD	Coastal and freshwater fish			

History of the Species in Ireland

The Red-throated Diver was first confirmed breeding in Donegal in 1884. Two pairs were reported in 1886 and two in 1948 (Kennedy *et al.* 1954). Since then the breeding population has probably fluctuated up to a maximum of about ten pairs. In 1968–1972 breeding was proved in three 10km squares and it was believed to be probably breeding in a fourth and possibly breeding in three more (Sharrock 1976).

Current Distribution and Status

Holarctic and circumpolar. The Red-throated Diver's southern breeding limit is about 60°N, descending to 50°N along oceanic margins (Cramp and Simmons 1977). Harrison (1982) gives the 18°C July isotherm as the southerly limit.

It breeds in west and north Scotland, Iceland, Fenno-Scandia and northern Russia and winters along the coast of south-west Iceland, north-west and west Europe, the north Mediterranean, the Black and Caspian Seas, eastern Asia and on the east and west coasts of North America.

Published breeding population estimates indicate 1,200–1,500 pairs in Scotland, 1,000 pairs in Norway (Batten *et al.* 1990), 2,000 pairs in Finland and 1,000 pairs in Iceland (Cramp and Simmons 1977).

In Ireland the Red-throated Diver breeds only in west Donegal although there were also reports of birds during the 1988–90 period of the New Breeding Atlas survey on the coast of Mayo and Galway (Gibbons *et al.* in press). The present population is considered to be less than ten pairs and probably no more than five pairs in any one year (J.R. Sheppard) although it is suggested (D. Norriss) that at least ten sites are occupied reasonably regularly, though not all simultaneously.

The population wintering in Irish coastal waters probably ranges from 200–300 and possibly up to 500 – a small proportion of the 10,000 or so known to winter in Irish and British coastal waters. In addition, there is a notable passage of birds along the south-east and east coast of Ireland in May (O.J. Merne).

Threats

Egg collecting was a problem in the years after breeding was first discovered but this is unlikely to be a problem at the present time. Disturbance has been shown to depress breeding in Shetland (Bundy 1978). In Ireland, however, most nesting sites are in remote and little visited locations, so the threats of egg collecting and visitor disturbance are not considered to be serious.

Habitat destruction by peat cutting and afforestation has already eliminated one nesting site (J.R. Sheppard) and several more are vulnerable to these threats. The presence of feral Mink in Donegal has been implicated in the desertion of one nesting site and other sites are undoubtedly at risk. Drift nets may present a further threat to birds feeding at sea. No nesting sites are protected at present.

Conservation

No conservation measures have been undertaken to date. Apparently no attempt has been made to visit all known nesting sites within one season since 1973, nor has there been any attempt to identify the ecological characteristics of the nesting and feeding sites. A comprehensive survey of the breeding population and the nesting and feeding habitats will be required before protection and management of the nesting and freshwater feeding sites can be undertaken.

BLACK-NECKED GREBE

Podiceps nigricollis **Rare**

RSPB/C.H. Gomersall

The Black-necked Grebe is a very rare and probably intermittent breeding bird in Ireland. It nests in reed beds at the edge of lowland lakes and its secretive habits make it hard to detect. It is an annual winter visitor in small numbers. As well as Ireland being at the north-western edge of the Eurasian part of its range, egg collecting in the past and continuing habitat destruction are likely reasons for its limited distribution and small numbers.

LEG STATUS IRL	RoI Protected	**LEG STATUS EUR**	Birds Dir	I
	NI Protected		Bern	II
INTL LEG STATUS			Bonn	–
OCCURRENCE IN IRELAND	[S],W	**BEZZEL INDEX, IRELAND**		15(B),16(W)
BREEDING PAIRS	Unknown (<10)	**WINTERING NUMBERS**		< 20
MAIN FOOD	Insects and other small invertebrates			

History of the Species in Ireland

Prior to 1900 the Black-necked Grebe was a rare winter visitor. The first record of attempted breeding was at Keel Lough, Achill, Mayo in 1906 (Hutchinson 1989) but breeding was not confirmed until 1915 at a turlough near Brierfield in Co. Roscommon. The breeding population peaked in the early 1930s when up to 300 nests were recorded in some years at Lough

Funshinagh, Roscommon, alone (Humphreys 1978). Up to ten pairs bred from 1949 to 1956 at Levally Lough near Tuam in Galway but ceased to do so when the Lough was drained (Ruttledge 1989). Subsequently the population declined to perhaps one pair by the late 1960s. Since the late 1960s there has been only one record of breeding in 1982 when Cotton and Hillis (1989) observed an adult male with four young at Lough Funshinagh. These authors report that they are not aware of any subsequent records of breeding Black-necked Grebes in Ireland although Hutchinson (1989) and O.J. Merne believe that small numbers of these secretive birds could still nest in Ireland.

Current Distribution and Status

Holarctic and Afro-tropical. The Black-necked Grebe breeds in Britain, in central, eastern and southern Europe north to Denmark and in southern Sweden. The European breeding population fluctuates from year to year but has shown a tendency to increase on the western and northern edges of its range in the past decade. The British population increased from less than 10 pairs prior to 1970 to 33 pairs in 1988 (Batten *et al.* 1990). There are, perhaps, 500–1,000 pairs breeding in N.W. Europe.

No breeding Black-necked Grebes were reported in Ireland during the 1988–90 period of the New Breeding Atlas survey (Gibbons *et al.* in press).

In winter it occurs in only very small numbers on the coast and on inland waters.

Threats

Drainage, habitat loss, disturbance, and possibly pollution are likely to have been major factors in the demise of the Black-necked Grebe population, though climatic change might be implicated, too. Natural water level fluctuations (e.g. at Lough Funshinagh) have also adversely affected the species (O.J. Merne). The presence of feral Mink in the nesting region suggests that any future breeding attempts could be hazardous.

Conservation

Two of its previously recorded nesting habitats are Wildfowl Sanctuaries, providing protection only against shooting in winter. There is a need, therefore, for comprehensive protection of these sites throughout the year and regular surveys to determine if and where Black-necked Grebes are breeding.

BITTERN

Botaurus stellaris — Extinct

RSPB/S.C. Porter

The Bittern was once a common breeding bird in Ireland, but ceased to breed about 1840. It favours lowland swamps with extensive shallow standing water and dense reedbeds with actively-encroaching reed margins. This species is now a rare winter visitor to Ireland but could become re-established if protected from illegal shooting and if suitable habitats are maintained.

LEG STATUS IRL	RoI Protected	**LEG STATUS EUR**	Birds Dir	I
	NI Protected		Bern	II
INTL LEG STATUS			Bonn	–
OCCURRENCE IN IRELAND	[W][S]	**BEZZEL INDEX, IRELAND**		–
BREEDING PAIRS	–	**WINTERING NUMBERS**		–
MAIN FOOD	Fish, frogs and freshwater invertebrates			

History of the Species in Ireland

Early in the last century the Bittern was recorded breeding in Antrim, Down, Donegal, Clare, Fermanagh, Kildare, Westmeath and Tipperary (Thompson

1849–56); Cork, Waterford, Galway, Mayo, Tyrone and Laois (Ussher & Warren 1900). Stewart (1831, cited by Thompson 1849–56) remarked that Bitterns were 'very common' in Donegal about 1800. The Bittern declined during the early 1800s and by 1840 it was considered extinct as a breeding bird (Ussher and Warren 1900) though this is contradicted by Thompson (1849–56) who said they were 'rather plentiful [in the 1840s] in the Dublin market which is supplied from several counties'. Thompson thought it may still have been breeding in inaccessible places in 1850. The decline of the Bittern was blamed on the 'drainage of the bogs and marshes' (Thompson 1849–56). It is clear that Bitterns were very widely shot, and this may also have been a factor in their decline. Bitterns were 'stated to be not uncommonly on sale in Ennis market' (Clare) until 1836 (Thompson 1849–56).

Since 1900 the Bittern has been a rare, mainly winter, visitor to Ireland with most occurrences in Cork and Waterford (Ruttledge 1966b).

Current Distribution and Status

Palaearctic, with breeding distribution covering Europe, North Africa and central and eastern Asia. Partially migratory, with some continental birds moving south and west in winter.

The European breeding population – excluding the former USSR – was estimated at 2,500–2,700 pairs in 1976, but the population subsequently declined by 30–50% following the cold winter of 1978/79 (Day 1981). The European strongholds are in France, Germany, the Netherlands and Sweden (Day 1981). The Bittern is declining throughout most of its European range (Cramp & Simmons 1977).

Britain was recolonised by Bitterns in 1911, following earlier extinction, and recorded a peak of 78–83 calling males ('boomers') in 1954 before declining again to 22–25 pairs in 1987. The most recent RSPB estimate for Britain is 18 calling males in 1992 (G. Williams).

The Bittern is now a rare visitor to Ireland, mainly in winter although booming birds have also been recorded. A Bittern was shot near Enniskillen, Fermanagh, in 1975 and a booming bird was heard at the same locality in April 1976 (NIBRC 1987). Booming birds were also present in Clare in 1982 and 1983 (Hutchinson 1989). One was caught and released near Lough Corrib in September 1989 (Whilde 1990).

Threats

Many visiting Bitterns, even in recent times, have been shot. Other potential hazards facing the British population – pesticide contamination, reed dieback and eutrophication (Batten *et al.* 1990) – are less acute in Ireland.

Conservation

The presence of booming birds in suitable breeding habitat indicates the potential for Bitterns to regain a foothold in Ireland. This will only be possible if, in future, booming birds are protected from illegal shooting and human disturbance. In the longer term protection and improvement of extensive reedbed systems through reserve purchase (e.g. at Portmore Lough, Antrim – now an RSPB reserve) will greatly assist the Bittern. Recent RSPB research has shown that Bitterns require larger territories than hitherto believed and favour areas where reedbeds are actively encroaching (G. Williams).

GADWALL

Anas strepera

Rare

O.J. Merne

The Gadwall is a scarce breeding duck and is thinly distributed in small numbers in winter, mainly on inland waters. It breeds close to water on the shores or islets of lakes with marginal reed beds. In Ireland the species is breeding at the western edge of its Eurasian range, though it has been slowly extending its range and increasing in numbers over the past fifty years. The British population arose in the mid-1800s from captured stock, possibly reinforced later by continental immigrants, which spread (Sharrock 1976) and, presumably, formed the basis of the Irish population.

LEG STATUS IRL	RoI Quarry	LEG STATUS EUR	Birds Dir	II/2
	NI Quarry		Bern	III
INTL LEG STATUS			Bonn	II
OCCURRENCE IN IRELAND	W[R]	BEZZEL INDEX, IRELAND		16(B),12(W)
BREEDING PAIRS	20–40	WINTERING NUMBERS		400–800
MAIN FOOD Aquatic plants				

History of the Species in Ireland

The Gadwall is a regular winter visitor. It was first recorded breeding in Armagh in 1933. Subsequently it bred in Fermanagh (1938) and on Lough Key in Roscommon (1940), in Kerry, on Lough Neagh and possibly in counties Cork, Donegal and Mayo (Kennedy *et al.* 1954) (Table 4).

TABLE 4 Numbers of breeding Gadwall at main Irish sites 1976 – 1988 (Hutchinson 1989; O'Sullivan and Smiddy 1988)

	'76	'77	'78	'79	'80	'81	'82	'83	'84	'85	'86	'87	'88
Lough Neagh	2	1	10				Regular breeder each year				17		20
Wexford		1	5					1			Up to 10 pairs per annum		
Cork		1				5		1			Probably regular breeder		5
Galway			1			3			Probably regular on L.Corrib			3	
Clare					1								
Limerick													1
Roscommon										1			1

Current Distribution and Status

Mainly Holarctic with some birds wintering in southern Asia and east Africa. The Gadwall is locally distributed as a breeding species in all EC countries except Italy and Portugal and locally but more widely distributed in winter throughout the EC and Iceland. It appears to be undergoing a slow extension of its range and an increase in numbers. The European breeding population is possibly 500–1,000 pairs, of which about 500 pairs breed in Britain (Owen *et al.* 1986) and the wintering population about 12,000 birds (Rüger *et al.* 1986). The British and Irish wintering total rose to over 6,000 by 1985/86 (Fox and Salmon 1989) and had reached 6,600 in 1988 (Batten *et al.* 1991).

In Ireland it is very locally distributed during the breeding season and thinly distributed during winter, being largely absent from the north-west and south-west, though it was once numerous (200+) at Akeragh Lough and Lough Gill in Kerry in the 1960s and 1970s (O.J. Merne). During the 1988–90 period of the New Breeding Atlas survey breeding was confirmed or probable in Antrim, Down, Armagh, Fermanagh, Galway, Cork and Wexford and birds were present but not confirmed breeding in Roscommon, Offaly, Tipperary and Limerick (Gibbons *et al.* in press). Reports were received of: a pair on Lough Funshinagh, Roscommon on 3 June 1987 (O'Sullivan and Smiddy 1988); a female and young on Lough Corrib in 1991; and a breeding pair at Murlach, Ballyconneely, Galway in 1991 (L. Lysaght).

The species is hand-reared and released by wildfowling clubs in Northern Ireland and Britain (D. Allen) and though the impact of this action on the size and status of the Irish population is unknown it is suspected that the breeding population in north-east Ireland (Down) is probably a mixture of wild and feral birds.

Threats

Drainage, habitat destruction, water pollution, disturbance and predation by gulls and mink are considered to be the major potential threats to breeding Gadwall but none has been quantified or studied in detail.

Conservation

The Gadwall is protected at some of its breeding sites in Northern Ireland and at several wintering sites. Strangford Lough and Lough Neagh are Areas of Special Scientific Interest and the Lough Neagh Islands are a National Nature Reserve. In the Republic it is protected only at Lady's Island Lake (breeding) and at several wintering sites which are Wildfowl Sanctuaries. There is an immediate need for a comprehensive survey of breeding populations, the protection of major breeding sites in the Republic and the removal of the species from the hunting list.

PINTAIL

Anas acuta

Rare

R.T. Mills

The Pintail is an extremely rare and possibly intermittent breeding duck, Ireland being at the south-western edge of its Eurasian range. It typically breeds near water but there are no details available of specific habitats used in Ireland. Its winter distribution is localised and flock sizes are generally quite small – the largest concentrations occurring on the coast at the North Bull (Dublin), Strangford Lough (Down) and Bannow Bay (Wexford) (Hutchinson 1989) and inland on the Little Brosna (Offaly), at Tacumshin Lake (Wexford) and Rahasane Turlough (Galway) (Sheppard in press).

LEG STATUS IRL	RoI Quarry	LEG STATUS EUR	Birds Dir	II/1,III/2
	NI Quarry		Bern	III
INTL LEG STATUS			Bonn	II
OCCURRENCE IN IRELAND	[S],W	BEZZEL INDEX, IRELAND		21(B),13(W)
BREEDING PAIRS	1+	WINTERING NUMBERS		4,000–7,500
MAIN FOOD	Aquatic plants and invertebrates			

History of the Species in Ireland

The Pintail is a regular winter visitor. It was long suspected of breeding in Ireland but the first nest with eggs was recorded only in 1917 in Roscommon. Subsequently it bred in Armagh (1923), Laois (1932), on an island in Strangford Lough, Down (1939 onwards though not in recent years, Brown 1990), in Wexford (1947) (Kennedy *et al.* 1954) and once in the period 1968–72 at Lough Beg, Londonderry and in Roscommon (Sharrock 1976). Since then the only records have been of single pairs at Lough Croan, Roscommon in 1978, 1979, 1981, 1983 and 1984 (Hutchinson 1989; J.P. Hillis) and, in 1984, a female with five young at Clonmacnoise on the River Shannon (Tubridy 1987). However, it is suspected (O.J. Merne) that the species has been overlooked and may well have been breeding on a regular basis in small numbers, particularly in the central Shannon catchment area.

Current Distribution and Status

Mainly Holarctic. The Pintail breeds locally in Iceland, Britain and in nearly all Continental countries largely north of a line from north-east France to Hungary. It is common in Fenno-Scandia but the breeding population in the EC is perhaps no more than 300–400 pairs.

In Ireland it is a very rare and perhaps intermittent breeder. During the 1988–90 period of the New Breeding Atlas survey a female with ten ducklings was recorded in Sligo (R.A. Chapman) and breeding was confirmed or probable in Down with birds reported, but not noted as breeding, in Antrim, Londonderry, Offaly and Clare (Gibbons *et al.* in press).

Threats

Drainage, habitat destruction, disturbance and predation are the main local threats to the establishment of a long-term breeding population of Pintail in Ireland.

Conservation

No measures have yet been taken to conserve breeding Pintail or their habitat in Ireland. It will, therefore, be necessary to survey all potential breeding sites and implement the protection of any which have potential for long-term use by breeding Pintail.

GARGANEY

Anas querquedula

Rare

Joe Blossom/NHPA

The Garganey is a rare breeding duck and a scarce but annual spring and autumn passage migrant through Ireland which is at the western edge of the Palaearctic part of its range. The species typically nests in dense emergent vegetation at the margins of lakes. However, there is no specific information available about its nesting habitat in Ireland.

The numbers reaching Britain vary from year to year, the biggest arrivals being in warm springs in anticyclonic conditions. The British breeding population is largest in years when a strong migration follows a period of wet weather, so that plenty of shallow pools have formed on water-meadows and coastal freshwater marshes (Sharrock 1976). Presumably these factors also apply in Ireland.

LEG STATUS IRL	RoI Protected	**LEG STATUS EUR**	Birds Dir	II/1
	NI Protected		Bern	III
INTL LEG STATUS			Bonn	II
OCCURRENCE IN IRELAND	S,[P]	**BEZZEL INDEX, IRELAND**		19(B)
BREEDING PAIRS	<10	**PASSAGE NUMBERS**		<50
MAIN FOOD	Aquatic plants and invertebrates			

History of the Species in Ireland

The Garganey was first recorded breeding at Lough Neagh in 1956 and in

Kerry in 1959 (Ruttledge 1966b). Since then breeding has been suggested by the presence of a pair at Lady's Island Lake, Wexford, in 1978, 1986, 1987 and 1988 and it is thought (O.J. Merne) that a very small population now breeds regularly in that area. It possibly bred on Pollardstown Fen, Kildare, in the recent past (O.J. Merne). A female was seen at Lough Beg in Londonderry in July 1986 but it is not known whether breeding occurred in the area and birds have been seen elsewhere on Lough Neagh in early summer without proof of breeding being established (J.S. Furphy).

Current Distribution and Status

The Garganey breeds throughout the Palaearctic and winters in central Africa and south-east Asia. It breeds locally in England, Wales, France, Belgium, northern Italy and more extensively in the Netherlands, Germany and Denmark. The European breeding population may be up to 8,000 pairs. The species increased in Europe in the twentieth century as the climate became milder (Reid Henry and Harrison 1988) so climatic warming might benefit the Garganey in Ireland. Birds were seen but not recorded as breeding during the 1988–90 period of the New Breeding Atlas survey in Down, Armagh, Fermanagh, Galway, Roscommon and Dublin (Gibbons *et al.* in press) and in Armagh, Antrim, Tyrone, Dublin, Kerry and Wexford in spring 1991 (*IWC News*, Autumn 1991). A family party with 4–5 juveniles was recorded at Tacumshin Lake, Wexford, in July-August 1990 (E. Dempsey).

Threats

Habitat destruction, disturbance and predation are likely to be the main threats to breeding Garganey. Droughts in sub-Saharan Africa may affect the numbers visiting Ireland.

Conservation

Two of the Garganey's possible breeding locations in Northern Ireland are Areas of Special Scientific Interest and a site in the Republic is designated for protection under Article 4 of the 'Birds Directive' and is also a Statutory Refuge for Fauna. A survey will be required of breeding sites outside the above mentioned protected areas and protection provided where Garganey do or could breed regularly.

SHOVELER

Anas clypeata **Rare**

INP/J. Malins

The Shoveler is an uncommon breeding species but widespread and fairly numerous in winter. The largest winter concentrations have been recorded inland on Lough Rea (Galway), Ballyallia Lough (Clare) and Rahasane Turlough (Galway) although the species also occurs at coastal wetlands (Sheppard in press). It nests in tussocky vegetation beside shallow, lowland mesotrophic to eutrophic lakes. In Ireland it is breeding at the edge of the European part of its range. The reasons for the spread of Shoveler in the early part of the century and the recent decline and contraction of its range are not known but could have been associated with habitat deterioration and climate change.

LEG STATUS IRL	RoI	Quarry	LEG STATUS EUR	Birds Dir	II/1, III/2
	NI	Quarry		Bern	III
INTL LEG STATUS				Bonn	II
OCCURRENCE IN IRELAND		R,W,P	BEZZEL INDEX, IRELAND		13(B),15(W)
BREEDING PAIRS		c 100	WINTERING NUMBERS		4,000–8,000

MAIN FOOD Seeds and plants, planktonic crustaceans and other invertebrates

History of the Species in Ireland

The Shoveler first bred in Ireland in 1863 and by the end of the last century there was evidence that it bred in many parts of the country and by the 1950s it had been recorded in 26 counties (Kennedy *et al.* 1954). At the present time, however, it appears to be much more restricted in its breeding distribution

(J. Greenwood). During the 1968–72 period it was confirmed to breed in nineteen 10km squares and was probably or possibly breeding in a further 31 squares, its overall distribution covering about fifteen counties (Sharrock 1976). Its strongholds at that time were around Lough Neagh and in Roscommon with scattered breeding pairs mainly in Galway, Mayo and Wexford. Subsequently, it has bred in small numbers in north and east Cork and Kildare. A survey in 1986 (Partridge 1986) indicated that the breeding population around Lough Neagh had declined to 20 pairs and that 34 pairs were present around Upper Lough Erne. In 1987 there were 12 pairs and 27 males on the Shannon Callows (Nairn *et al.* 1988).

Current Distribution and Status

Holarctic and wintering in Africa and southern Asia. The Shoveler breeds extensively in Britain, Denmark and the Netherlands and locally in EC countries to the south. The European breeding population is 12–16,000 pairs. About 175,000 winter in Europe, locally in most EC countries.

In recent years the breeding population has declined on the east coast but appears to be holding its own at Ring Marsh and Tacumshin Lake in Wexford (O.J. Merne). During the 1988–90 period of the New Breeding Atlas survey breeding was confirmed or probable in Antrim, Down, Armagh, Fermanagh, Sligo, Roscommon and Offaly with further records of birds in Londonderry, Tyrone, Donegal, Cavan, Mayo, Galway, Limerick, Tipperary and Cork (Gibbons *et al.* in press). Two nests with eggs were recorded on Bullock Island in the River Shannon in Offaly and one possible nest on Dernish Island on Upper Lough Erne (Fermanagh) in 1991 (I.J. Herbert).

Threats

Drainage, habitat destruction, disturbance and predation pose the greatest threats to breeding Shoveler.

Conservation

A small number of pairs nest in protected areas (Areas of Special Scientific Interest and National Nature Reserves) in Northern Ireland but apparently no breeding sites are protected in the Republic. A survey of actual and potential breeding habitats is required along with protection of the main current breeding sites. If the winter population is confirmed to be about 4,200 a curtailment of hunting of this species should be considered.

POCHARD

Aythya ferina

Rare

R.T. Mills

The Pochard is a rare breeding duck but numerous in the winter when large flocks, composed mainly of males, visit some of the larger lakes in the north, west and midlands. It usually nests in reed beds beside large pools, lakes or slow moving rivers. Ireland is at the western edge of its Palaearctic range and this probably contributes to its scarcity as a breeding species.

LEG STATUS IRL	RoI	Quarry	**LEG STATUS EUR**	Birds Dir	II/1,III/2
	NI	Quarry		Bern	III
INTL LEG STATUS				Bonn	II
OCCURRENCE IN IRELAND		S,W	**BEZZEL INDEX, IRELAND**		12(B),11(W)
BREEDING PAIRS		30+	**WINTERING NUMBERS**		

30,000–50,000

MAIN FOOD Aquatic plants and (mainly freshwater) invertebrates

History of the Species in Ireland

The breeding of Pochard was first suspected at the beginning of the century and the initial confirmation was in Monaghan in 1907. A few pairs nested in Roscommon between 1930 and 1934, a nest with eggs was found in Laois in 1931, two pairs bred in Galway in 1950, 1951 and 1952 and two pairs bred in Tipperary in 1952. Breeding may also have occurred in Donegal and on

Lough Erne (Kennedy *et al.* 1954). During the 1968–72 period Pochard were confirmed breeding in nine 10km squares and probably or possibly nesting in forty squares, mainly in the middle third of the country. As these results were the combined observations of five summers they may have exaggerated the numbers involved in any one year. Since 1972 breeding has been recorded at ten sites in eight counties.

Current Distribution and Status

Palaearctic and wintering in Africa and southern Asia. The Pochard breeds throughout much of Britain, where the population was estimated to be 370–395 pairs in 1986 (Fox 1991). It also breeds widely in Denmark and locally in the Netherlands, Germany, Belgium, France and Spain. The European breeding population is 4,000–5,000 pairs. It winters extensively throughout Britain, the Netherlands, Belgium, France and Spain and locally in Germany, Italy, Portugal and Greece. The European wintering population has been declining since the peak of the mid-1970s (Owen *et al.* 1986) and now stands at about 350,000 birds of which about 50,000 winter in Ireland, including up to 41,000 on Lough Neagh (Winfield *et al.* 1989; Kirby *et al.* 1991).

In Ireland, during the 1988–90 period of the New Breeding Atlas survey breeding was confirmed or probable in Antrim, Roscommon and Longford and birds were seen but not reported to be breeding in Antrim, Down, Tyrone, Fermanagh, Mayo, Galway, Offaly, Westmeath, Meath, Kildare, Tipperary, Limerick, Cork and Wexford (Gibbons *et al.* in press). In Roscommon in May 1991 six pairs were present on Lough Croan and two pairs on Lough Funshinagh (K. Kane). A female and young were reported on Lough Corrib in 1991. The Lough Neagh population is estimated to be around 20 pairs (R. D. Davidson).

Threats

Drainage, habitat destruction, disturbance and predation are the main threats to breeding Pochard.

Conservation

Some Pochard nest in protected areas in Northern Ireland but no known breeding sites in the Republic are protected. A survey of breeding habitats and protection of the regular breeding haunts will be required in the near future.

COMMON SCOTER

Melanitta nigra **Endangered**

RSPB/D. Green

The Common Scoter is a rare breeding species which nests in small numbers on some of the larger western and midland lakes. In winter it occurs in larger numbers mainly off the north-east and south-west coasts (Sheppard in press). It nests in dense scrub and grass on small lake islands and feeds in shallow waters nearby. In Ireland it is breeding at the extreme south-western edge of its Palaearctic range. During the past twenty years its numbers have declined largely, it is believed, as a result of deteriorating water quality on Lower Lough Erne which led to a reduction in its food supply, possibly predation by feral Mink on sitting females, and competition for food with introduced Roach (Partridge 1989).

LEG STATUS IRL	RoI Protected	**LEG STATUS EUR**	Birds Dir	II/3,III/3
	NI Protected		Bern	III
INTL LEG STATUS			Bonn	II
OCCURRENCE IN IRELAND	S,W	**BEZZEL INDEX, IRELAND**		27(B),13(W)
BREEDING PAIRS	65–75	**WINTERING NUMBERS**		3,000–5,000

MAIN FOOD Benthic molluscs, other invertebrates and small fish

History of the Species in Ireland

The Common Scoter was first recorded breeding on Lower Lough Erne in 1905 (though it had probably bred in 1904). Numbers increased to seven pairs in 1917, to at least 50 pairs by 1950 and to 140–150 pairs by the late 1960s after which a marked decline set in (Table 5 and Figure 3).

Common Scoters were first seen on Lough Conn during the breeding season in about 1938 but breeding was not confirmed until 1948. Subsequently, numbers increased to 28–30 pairs in 1968 since when the population appears to have remained static through 1983 (29 pairs, Ruttledge 1987) to 1987 (32 pairs, Partridge and Smith 1988). Breeding appears to have started on the adjoining Lough Cullin in 1971 and by 1983 it was reported that at least 24 pairs were present there. However, Partridge (cited by Hutchinson 1989) suggests that Lough Cullin is used as a feeding and loafing area and that this was an over-estimate of the breeding population which in 1987 was only six pairs (Partridge and Smith 1988).

Common Scoters were first reported on Lough Corrib in the late 1970s (B. Curran) and at least four pairs were confirmed breeding in 1981, the population rising to seven pairs in 1983 (Whilde 1983) and ten pairs in 1987

TABLE 5 Numbers of breeding pairs of Common Scoter counted at various sites, 1967–1992 (Based on Hutchinson 1989, Partridge 1989 and J. Magee) P = Present, * = Incomplete count

	Lower Lough Erne	Lough Conn	Lough Cullin	Lough Ree	Lough Corrib	Lough Carra	Assaroe Lough
1967	152					P	
1968		28–30					P
1969	115					1	P
1970	127					P	
1971	105	1+		P			
1972	80*	1+					
1973	116						
1974	116			P			
1975	121						
1976	107						
1977	121						
1978	113			P			
1979	87						
1980	87						
1981	63				4+		
1982	73						
1983	51	29+	24+		7		
1984	46			30+	7		
1985	11*			30+	7		
1986	21				7		
1987	10	32	6	10–20	10		
1988	7				P		
1989	9				P		
1990	6				P		
1991	2				P		
1992	5				P		
1993	0				P		

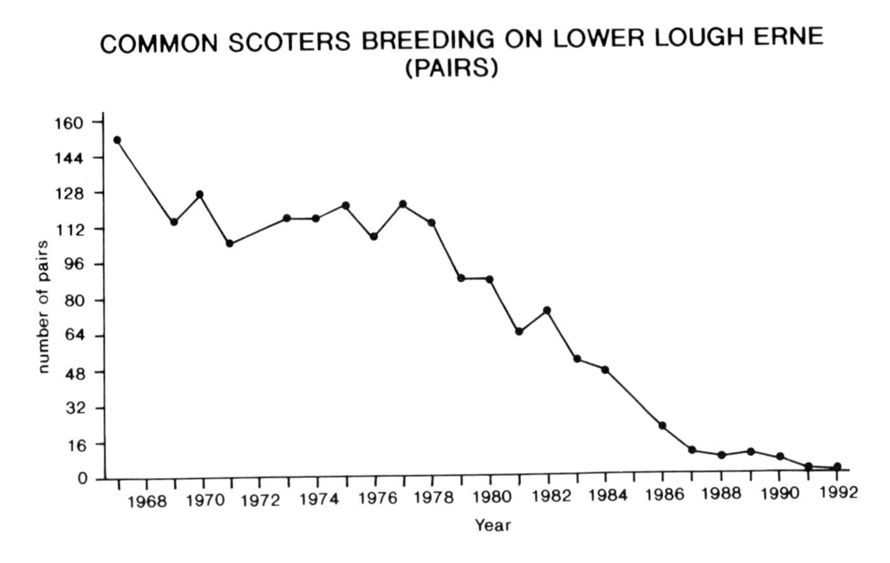

Fig 3 Decline in numbers of Common Scoters (pairs) breeding on Lower Lough Erne, 1967–1992 (Source: Partridge 1989; J. Magee, RSPB).

(Partridge and Smith 1988). A Common Scoter was first reported on Lough Ree in the breeding season of 1971 but it was not until 1985 that at least 30 pairs were reported to be breeding there. The minimum estimate for 1985/86 was given as 40 pairs (Ruttledge 1987). However, this may also have been an over-estimate because Partridge and Smith (1988) reported only 10–20 pairs on Lough Ree in 1987. In recent years there have been unconfirmed reports of breeding on Lough Melvin, Leitrim (D.C. Cotton).

Current Distribution and Status

Northern Palaearctic, north-west and north-east Nearctic. In Europe the Common Scoter breeds in Iceland (500 pairs), Finland (500 pairs), Scotland (about 100 pairs), Norway and Sweden (large numbers but no data to hand). The current distribution and status in Ireland have been indicated above. Despite the decline, Ireland holds about 40% of the EC breeding Common Scoter population.

Outside the breeding season up to 1,500,000 have been recorded on spring passage in Finland but it is estimated that the north-west European wintering population is more likely to be about 400,000–500,000 birds (Owen *et al.* 1986, Boyd and Pirot 1989).

Threats

The threats mentioned earlier continue on Lough Erne. On Lough Conn the water quality has remained high and the quantity and quality of Common

Scoter food satisfactory. The major potential threats here would, therefore, appear to be disturbance and predation by feral Mink which have been present in the area since 1987. On Lough Corrib water quality is likely to remain satisfactory for the foreseeable future. However, Roach, which were introduced to the system in the 1970s, have now colonised the whole lake and could adversely affect the food availability for Common Scoter. Feral Mink have been recorded to the east of the Corrib catchment and it is only a matter of time before they enter the system. Disturbance is likely to increase with the development of recreational activities on and around the lough.

Roach and feral Mink are present in Lough Ree, pollution is increasing and recreational disturbance is probably greater there than in the western loughs. It is likely that Common Scoters are on the decline in Lough Ree (Partridge, 1989).

Conservation

The Bezzel Index of 27 is one of the highest recorded for an Irish species and clearly indicates the conservation importance of the Common Scoter.

Common Scoters on Lough Erne nested partly on an RSPB Reserve at Castle Caldwell and partly on a National Nature Reserve (Castle Archdale Islands). Otherwise no breeding sites are protected in Northern Ireland or in the Republic.

The major conservation requirements for breeding Common Scoter include:

- pollution abatement and investigation on Lough Ree and Lough Erne (investigation currently under way on Lough Erne as part of a cross-border study);
- maintenance of water quality and low disturbance levels at the other major haunts;
- careful monitoring of the breeding population and breeding success, particularly on western loughs as feral Mink arrive;
- protection of nesting sites from feral Mink (now under way on Lough Erne);
- investigation of competition between Common Scoter and introduced Roach;
- legal protection of main nesting and feeding areas on each of the major loughs;
- inclusion of the Common Scoter in Annex I of the EC Birds Directive.

GOOSANDER

Mergus merganser **Rare**

RSPB/H. Arndt

The Goosander is a very rare breeding duck and a winter visitor in small numbers. Breeding Goosanders favour clear, fast flowing, salmonid rivers and nest in tree holes, burrows and amongst rocks on the ground (Owen *et al.* 1986). The current nesting locations of the Goosander in Donegal are not known and no systematic observations of the species have been made since the early 1980s. In Ireland the Goosander is at the south-western edge of the Eurasian part of its range.

LEG STATUS IRL	RoI Protected	**LEG STATUS EUR**	Birds Dir	II/2
	NI Protected		Bern	III
INTL LEG STATUS			Bonn	II
OCCURRENCE IN IRELAND	S,W	**BEZZEL INDEX, IRELAND**		18(B)
BREEDING PAIRS	1–2	**WINTERING NUMBERS**		20–30
MAIN FOOD	Freshwater fish, marine fish in winter			

History of the Species in Ireland

The breeding of Goosanders was proved for the first time in Donegal in 1969 and was repeated in the years 1970, 1971, 1974 to 1978 inclusive, and 1989. Birds were seen in the breeding habitat in 1978 to 1981 but breeding was not proved by the sighting of unfledged young as in other years. Goosanders were not recorded in the breeding habitat in 1972, 1973 and from 1982 to 1988 inclusive (Sheppard 1978; Hutchinson 1989; O'Sullivan and Smiddy 1990). A pair was seen at Carrowmore Lake, Mayo, in April 1991 (A. Walsh) but there were no later reports to indicate that breeding occurred. However, although breeding has only been proved once since 1981, the presence of this sedentary species in winter (e.g. four in 1990) suggests that it may still breed regularly in Donegal (J.R. Sheppard, C. O'Keefe).

Current Distribution and Status

Holarctic and boreal with some wintering in southern Asia. The Goosander breeds in Iceland, Fenno-Scandia, northern and western Britain and locally in the north and east of the EC with a population of up to 10,000 pairs, of which 915–1,246 nest in Britain. The European wintering population is probably between 75,000 and 150,000. In Ireland the Goosander is confined to Donegal as a confirmed breeding species, but the possibility of it nesting in suitable habitat elsewhere should not be overlooked.

Threats

As so little is known about the ecology of the Goosander in Ireland it can only be surmised that disturbance, predation (possibly by feral Mink) and conifer afforestation could pose threats to its continued breeding which has, in the past, been characterised by low productivity in Donegal. Rhododendron clearance, started in earnest in the late 1970s in the Glenveagh National Park, could have disturbed birds at their original nesting site (C. O'Keefe). Shooting on game fishing waters could be a further threat.

Continued legal culling of Goosanders in Scotland may be reducing the possibility of immigration into Ireland as a periodic supplementation of the small Irish population.

Conservation

Goosanders are probably breeding in a National Park. The conservation of these, and of others breeding outside the Park, requires the location and monitoring of breeding birds and the protection of their nesting and feeding habitats.

WHITE-TAILED EAGLE

Haliaeetus albicilla **Extinct**

RSPB/W. Suetens

Early in the last century the White-tailed Eagle, also known as the Sea Eagle, was breeding widely around the British and Irish coasts and at some inland sites. It suffered heavy persecution at the hands of gamekeepers, egg collectors, sportsmen and landowners so that it was extinct in Ireland by about 1910 and in Britain by 1918. It is largely a coastal species feeding on seabirds, fish, larger mammals and carrion (Batten *et al.* 1990). The bird has survived in considerable numbers in Norway from where it was re-introduced to Britain in 1975. Within the last two years a captive-breeding programme has been established in Cork with the intention of re-establishing a wild breeding population in Ireland.

LEG STATUS IRL	RoI Protected	**LEG STATUS EUR**	Birds Dir	I
	NI Protected		Bern	II
INTL LEG STATUS	UN R, IUCN R		Bonn	II
OCCURRENCE IN IRELAND	[W][S]	**BEZZEL INDEX, IRELAND**		–
BREEDING PAIRS	–	**WINTERING NUMBERS**		–

MAIN FOOD Seabirds, fish, larger mammals and carrion

History of the Species in Ireland

The White-tailed Eagle bred mostly on marine cliffs in Munster, Connaught and Ulster until the early 1900s when it became extinct. The species was plentiful in Thompson's (1849–56) time and he reported seeing five mature birds on Horn Head, Donegal. The White-tailed Eagle bred widely throughout Ireland and, apart from marine cliffs, apparently bred in the Mournes, on lake islands in Connemara and on Lugnaquillia in Wicklow (Thompson 1849–56). By 1900 the species was confined to the most remote parts of Kerry and Mayo (Ussher and Warren 1900) and was said to have disappeared a few years later (Ruttledge 1966b).

Current Distribution and Status

Palaearctic and south-west Greenland. The species is widespread in eastern Europe and across the former USSR (Batten *at al.* 1990), the bulk of the population breeding north of the 40°N parallel. It is generally linked to sea coasts, lake shores, broad rivers and wetlands where fish and other aquatic prey is plentiful. There has been a marked decline in range since the 19th century due to persecution, poisoning and pesticides with the remaining European strongholds on the Norwegian coast (450 pairs), North Germany (120 pairs), Sweden (61 pairs), Finland (26 pairs) and the Volga Delta, former USSR (*c* 150 pairs) (Cramp and Simmons 1980).

Between 1975 and 1985, 82 young birds were brought to Britain from Norway and released on Rhum. The first pairs attempted to breed in the early 1980s and the first juvenile was fledged in 1985 (Batten *et al.* 1990). In 1992 four pairs nested successfully, raising seven young (G. Williams).

Since becoming extinct as a breeding species the White-tailed Eagle has been a rare visitor to Ireland with three records since 1965 (Hutchinson 1989). The last of these was a wing-tagged bird on Rathlin Island, Antrim, in April 1985 which had been released as a juvenile on Rhum in 1982 (NIBRC 1987). Birds were also recorded near Mullingar in winter 1991–92 and at Lower Lough Corrib in December 1992.

Threats

The White-tailed Eagle, like many other birds of prey, suffered greatly from human persecution in the 18th and 19th centuries. Thompson's (1849–56) statement that thirteen or fourteen eagles were killed at Horn Head within four years indicates the scale of the destruction. The widespread use of strychnine in poison baits was also an important factor but the sale and use of strychnine for vermin control has now been banned (*IWC News* Spring 1992). However, despite this the poisoning problem remains and is a major threat facing the re-introduced White-tailed Eagles along with the risk of illegal shooting, human disturbance and concerns about the availability of sufficient wild prey.

Conservation

A twenty-year programme to re-introduce White-tailed Eagles to Ireland was launched in 1991, following an earlier feasibility study by the Irish Wildbird Conservancy (Whilde 1986). It is intended to establish two small groups of 8–10 Eagles on the Blasket Islands, Kerry, and possibly later on Clare Island, Mayo, from captive-bred stock. The German Raptor Research Centre at Guttenburg will provide birds to Fota Wildlife Park, Cork, for the breeding programme and also for release (McKeown 1991). The first pair of White-tailed Eagles was released into the wild on Inishvickillane in April 1992 (*IWC News* Summer 1992).

MARSH HARRIER

Circus aeruginosus

Extinct

Hellio & Van Ingen/NHPA

The Marsh Harrier has been extinct in Ireland as a breeding species since 1917. It was formerly widespread but declined, mainly due to human persecution. In recent years, however, the species has been visiting Ireland in increasing numbers and there is a possibility it will recommence breeding soon. In Britain it breeds among reeds or sedges, usually within extensive reed beds. It usually hunts over open country dominated by aquatic vegetation, or on agricultural land, birds, rabbits and small mammals being the main prey (Batten *et al.* 1990).

LEG STATUS IRL	RoI Protected	**LEG STATUS EUR**	Birds Dir	I
	NI Protected		Bern	II
INTL LEG STATUS			Bonn	II
OCCURRENCE IN IRELAND	[W][S]	**BEZZEL INDEX, IRELAND**		–
BREEDING PAIRS	–	**WINTERING NUMBERS**		–
MAIN FOOD	Birds, rabbits and small mammals			

History of the Species in Ireland

Before 1840 the Marsh Harrier was widely distributed in Ireland. Among the counties in which it bred Thompson (1849–56) mentions Kerry, Cork, Tipperary, Monaghan, Tyrone, Down, Antrim and Londonderry. Watters (1853) described it as the most abundant of our larger birds of prey and widely distributed. By 1890 its numbers had been greatly reduced by shooting and poisoning but it still maintained a 'precarious existence' on the midland bogs and in parts of Galway (Ussher and Warren 1900). The Marsh Harrier became extinct as a breeding species by 1917 but single birds lingered on in Laois up to 1935 (Kennedy *et al.* 1954). From 1941 to 1965 the species was recorded about every other year, mostly in eastern counties.

Current Distribution and Status

The Eurasian race *C. a. aeruginosus* occurs in the western Palaearctic, except North Africa, and eastwards to northern Mongolia and Lake Baikal (Cramp and Simmons 1980). Large populations exist in some European countries e.g. the Netherlands 800–900 pairs, Denmark 500 pairs, Sweden 520 pairs, former West Germany 725–850 pairs, former East Germany 1,800+ pairs, France 700–1,000 pairs, Spain 500 pairs and Poland 2,000 pairs. Populations in north-west Europe have generally been increasing over the last 10–15 years (Batten *et al.* 1990; Cramp and Simmons 1980).

The British population became extinct by 1900 but regular breeding started again in 1927 and numbers have built up to 86 breeding females in 1990 (J.C.U. Day).

The expanding European population is reflected in Irish records with birds reported almost every year since 1966 and as many as thirteen records per year. A male constructed nest platforms in Clare in May 1981 and Hutchinson (1989) suggested a resumption of breeding might be imminent.

Threats

Although greatly reduced in scale, illegal shooting and poisoning are still a serious threat to visiting birds. Habitat loss could also be considered important and, as in Britain (Batten *et al.* 1990), the small size of many breeding sites could make birds more susceptible to disturbance.

Conservation

The protection of potential nest sites such as extensive reed beds will encourage the re-establishment of breeding birds in Ireland. Clearly, if and when birds do recommence breeding, the nest sites will have to be fully guarded.

HEN HARRIER

Circus cyaneus

Endangered

R.T. Mills

The Hen Harrier is a large bird of prey which ranges widely throughout Ireland, although its numbers are small. It breeds on moorlands, in young conifer plantations and in clear-felled areas from 150m to 400m in altitude (O'Flynn 1983), particularly, but by no means exclusively, in areas overlying Old Red Sandstone (Sharrock 1976). Primarily a ground-nesting bird, an unusual instance of tree-nesting has been reported recently from Antrim (Scott *et al.* 1991). Outside the breeding season it can also be seen over lake margins, reed beds, saltmarshes, farmland (stubbles), marginal farmland and cutaway bog.

The Hen Harrier's low numbers can be ascribed to a reduction in its breeding and feeding habitats through the clearance of bog, scrub and marginal land for agriculture and forestry, and the maturation of forest plantations (O'Flynn 1983). Fox predation of nests has led to low productivity in some areas (J.K. Partridge) and it has been suggested that the recovery of the species in Wicklow has been adversely affected by the aggressive behaviour of Peregrines (Hutchinson 1989).

LEG STATUS IRL	RoI Protected	**LEG STATUS EUR**	Birds Dir	I
	NI Protected		Bern	III
INTL LEG STATUS			Bonn	II
OCCURRENCE IN IRELAND	R	**BEZZEL INDEX, IRELAND**		17(B)
BREEDING PAIRS	c 50–70	**WINTERING NUMBERS**		<150
MAIN FOOD	Birds and small mammals			

History of the Species in Ireland

The Hen Harrier was widely distributed throughout Ireland in the first half of the nineteenth century but had declined by 1900 and was considered to be breeding only in Antrim, Cork, Dublin, Galway, Kerry, Laois, Limerick, Offaly, Tipperary and Waterford, having disappeared from Down, Fermanagh, Londonderry and Wicklow (Hutchinson 1989). However, it is likely that it was never numerous in the nineteenth century (O'Flynn 1983). It was thought to have become extinct by the 1950s (Kennedy *et al.* 1954) but had, in fact, continued to breed in the Slieve Bloom Mountains, Laois and Offaly, and on the Waterford – Tipperary border (Watson 1977).

The population started to recover in the early 1950s and by 1964 at least 35 pairs were known to be breeding in six counties: Cork, Kilkenny, Laois, Waterford, Wexford and Wicklow (Ruttledge 1966b; O'Flynn 1983). By 1972 it was estimated that 200–300 pairs were breeding in sixteen counties and that this population level was maintained until the late 1970s when a marked decline set in, except in Antrim, Tyrone, Kerry and mid-Cork where the species was increasing or holding its own (O'Flynn 1983). Subsequently, the Hen Harrier was considered to be declining in Northern Ireland as well (J.S. Furphy cited by Hutchinson 1989) but it has increased again in recent years (J. Whiteside). In Cork and Kerry the population has been holding its own overall, although it has almost disappeared from some areas, largely because of the burning of hill vegetation.

Current Distribution and Status

Holarctic. *C. c. cyaneus* breeds in a broad zone across Europe and Asia between 40°N and 70°N, east to the Kamchatka peninsula and winters mainly in southern Asia and western and southern Europe. *C. c. hudsonius* breeds in North America. The European breeding population is probably in the order of 6,000–7,000 pairs, including 2,800–3,800 in France, 1,000–2,000 in Sweden, 500 in Spain, 500+ in Britain (Bibby 1990), 200 in Germany, over 100 in the Netherlands and 10 in Norway (Batten *et al.* 1990). The British population has declined since the early 1970s. However, Hen Harriers colonised the Isle of Man in 1977 and the population increased to over 80 in 1990 (Cullen 1991). There is no information available on trends elsewhere.

In Ireland it is locally distributed, mainly in the southern part of the country. In 1982 the population was estimated to be 72 pairs (Clarke and Watson

1990). There are no recent estimates available but it is considered that there may be no more than 50–70 pairs still breeding. During the 1988–90 period of the New Breeding Atlas survey breeding was confirmed or probable in Antrim, Tyrone, Fermanagh (several pairs, J. Whiteside), Galway, Clare, Laois, Tipperary, Limerick, Kerry, Cork and Waterford. Birds were also recorded in Londonderry, Mayo, Roscommon, Dublin, Wicklow, Carlow, Kilkenny and Wexford (Gibbons *et al.* in press).

In winter Hen Harriers range more widely and can be seen in most parts of the country, though they are rarest in the north-east (Hutchinson 1989). Some roost communally and twelve winter roosts were reported during the period 1983–1986 (Clarke and Watson 1990). The winter population is probably less than 150 birds.

Threats

The Hen Harrier population is threatened by further land reclamation, particularly of heather moorland and marginal farms, habitat loss through afforestation, burning, predation of nests and persecution on grouse moors and elsewhere. In Britain concern is being expressed about the progressive decline in clutch size of the Hen Harrier since 1978 (Crick *et al.* 1992). If a similar decline is occurring in Ireland it could exacerbate the difficulties already generated for the species by the activities mentioned above.

Conservation

No conservation measures have yet been introduced for the Hen Harrier although in the Republic part of the Slieve Bloom Mountains, a Hen Harrier stronghold, is a National Nature Reserve and part has been designated an Environmentally Sensitive Area. A National Park is being established in the Wicklow Mountains habitat. In Northern Ireland the species occurs in areas in northern Antrim and Fermanagh which have been designated as Environmentally Sensitive Areas.

There is a need for a comprehensive survey of the breeding population and communal roosts and the maintenance, enhancement and protection of its remaining breeding and roosting habitat. Further information is also required on its winter distribution and habitats.

GOLDEN EAGLE

Aquila chrysaetos

Extinct

RSPB/C.H. Gomersall

Like the White-tailed Eagle, the Golden Eagle became extinct in Ireland about 1910–1912, having been relatively common and widespread in the early 19th century. The species inhabits sparsely-populated upland regions in Europe and has generally declined because of human persecution and habitat loss. Its food consists mainly of mammals and birds. In Scotland Red Grouse, hares, rabbits, young sheep and Red Deer are the main items, the latter two taken mainly as carrion (Batten *et al.* 1990). As a rare visitor the conservation of the species in Ireland is not an issue at present although re-introduction may be considered in the future. The National Parks and Wildlife Service have recently assessed live prey and carrion density within a potential hunting range in Donegal.

LEG STATUS IRL	RoI Protected	**LEG STATUS EUR**	Birds Dir	I
	NI Protected		Bern	II
INTL LEG STATUS			Bonn	II
OCCURRENCE IN IRELAND	[W][S]	**BEZZEL INDEX, IRELAND**		–
BREEDING PAIRS	–	**WINTERING NUMBERS**		–
MAIN FOOD	Larger mammals and birds			

History of The Species in Ireland

The species formerly bred extensively on the higher ranges of Munster, Connaught and Ulster. Ussher and Warren (1900) wrote that '... within the last fifty years gamekeepers and shepherds have so successfully employed gun, trap and poison, while the eggs and young of the remaining birds have been so systematically taken, that this noble species has been nearly swept off the land'. Breeding ceased in Donegal in 1910 and in Mayo in about 1912, but non breeding individuals were recorded in Donegal, Mayo and Antrim up to 1930. A pair bred on Fair Head, Antrim from 1953 to 1960 with birds still present until 1962 (NIBRC 1987). Young were fledged in all years except 1956 (Ruttledge 1966b).

Current Distribution and Status

Holarctic. Six races are recognised throughout its range which covers Europe, north-west Africa, Asia and North America. In Europe it is found in mainly mountainous regions where human population density is low and disturbance minimal. The species has shown a marked contraction in range and numbers since the 19th century. More recently the population has shown some recovery in Britain, Fenno-Scandia and parts of central Europe. Figures for important European populations in the 1970s are – France 100–150 pairs, Spain – *c* 400 pairs, Norway 250–500 pairs, Sweden *c* 150 pairs, Finland 100+ pairs, Switzerland 100–200 pairs and Italy 120–150 pairs (Cramp and Simmons 1980).

In Britain the Golden Eagle is virtually restricted to Scotland where the population was drastically reduced by human persecution during the 19th century. During this century numbers have gradually recovered from 190 pairs in the early 1950s to 300 pairs in 1968 and 424 pairs in 1982 (Batten *et al.* 1990). This is still below its potential ceiling in Scotland of 600 pairs (Dennis *et al.* 1984). The Golden Eagle is now a rare visitor to Ireland with most records in Antrim (Hutchinson 1989), presumably Scottish birds.

Threats

Threats to visiting birds include shooting and poisoning. In Scotland there is concern about continuing habitat loss – and resulting prey scarcity – due to overgrazing, excessive burning and blanket afforestation (Watson *et al.* 1987). These comments apply equally to Ireland where in many places habitat conditions may not now be suitable for Golden Eagles, because of land use intensification. However, proposed reforms of the Common Agricultural Policy may lead to a reduction in overgrazing with a consequent improvement in habitat for some of the Golden Eagle's prey species.

Conservation

No conservation measures are required at present. The question of re-introducing the Golden Eagle to Ireland might arise in the future, in which case a detailed feasibility study will first be required.

MERLIN

Falco columbarius

Rare

R.T. Mills

The Merlin is Ireland's smallest and most unobtrusive raptor. It requires open ground for hunting and has a preference for dry moors with heather (Bibby and Natrass 1986) and bracken (Haworth and Thompson 1990) and tends to avoid wetter areas with Cotton-grass, Purple Moor-grass or Mat-grass which are managed for sheep (Haworth and Fielding 1988). It nests in lake island scrub, woodland and conifer plantations – the use of the latter habitat probably being under-estimated (D. Norriss). In 1986 two pairs out of twenty were ground nesting, but by 1991 the transition to tree nesting was complete in the study areas of the National Parks and Wildlife Service (D. Norriss). Outside the breeding season the Merlin ranges widely and can be seen in a variety of inland habitats and at the coast where it is attracted by flocks of finches and small waders (Lack 1986).

LEG STATUS IRL	RoI Protected	**LEG STATUS EUR**	Birds Dir	I
	NI Protected		Bern	II
INTL LEG STATUS			Bonn	II
OCCURRENCE IN IRELAND	R	**BEZZEL INDEX, IRELAND**		23(B)
BREEDING PAIRS	c 100+	**WINTERING NUMBERS**		300–500
MAIN FOOD	Small birds and large insects			

History of the Species in Ireland

The Merlin, which was never common in Ireland, was probably declining during the first part of this century (Kennedy *et al.* 1954) and by the early 1970s it was considered to be one of our scarcest birds of prey (Hutchinson 1989). In 1968–72 breeding was proved or believed probable in 102 10km squares (Sharrock 1976). In Dublin and Wicklow in 1986 breeding was proved in four 10km squares, probable in five and possible in ten (Noonan 1988). In the early 1980s breeding was proved in 6–7 squares, but as the original survey was not sufficiently thorough it is not wise to infer a trend from these figures (Noonan 1988). The current population trend is difficult to establish because the species appears to be adapting to new breeding habitats and to be adopting different behaviour patterns. Numbers may have been reduced locally by habitat loss (e.g. particularly as a result of afforestation in Northern Ireland; J.K. Partridge). But with the shift to conifer plantations some pairs may have been overlooked and any reported decline may have been more apparent than real.

Current Distribution and Status

Holarctic. The Merlin breeds in North America, Iceland, Britain, Fenno-Scandia and the Baltic states across Russia. Some northern breeders winter in Central and South America, southern Europe, North Africa and southern Asia (Batten *et al.* 1990). In Britain the breeding population has declined since about 1950 to an estimated total of 550–650 pairs in 1983–84 (Bibby and Nattrass 1986). The British wintering population is 1,500 to 2,000 birds.

In Ireland the Merlin is widely distributed but restricted during the breeding season mainly to areas of moorland, mountains and blanket bog. Out of a total breeding population of over 100 pairs 20 to 30 nest in Northern Ireland, 20 to 30 in Wicklow (in 1982, Hutchinson 1989), up to 12 in south Connemara (Haworth 1987) and 1–2 pairs in Sligo (D.C. Cotton). Densities of 3.8–7.8 pairs per 100km square have been recorded in three study areas in Donegal and Wicklow (D. Norriss). In Northern Ireland in 1989 out of a total of 31 breeding sites used during the past ten years 20 were occupied and breeding was confirmed in 14 of these (Partridge and Bellamy, in prep.). During the 1988–90 period of the New Breeding Atlas survey breeding was confirmed or probable in thirteen counties and birds were recorded in a further twelve counties (Gibbons *et al.* in press). A significant proportion (15–18%) of EC Merlins breeds in Ireland.

In winter Merlins occur mainly at the coast and inland on midland bogs. They are usually seen singly outside the breeding season (Hutchinson 1989). The winter population is probably in the range of 300–500 birds.

Threats

The impacts of habitat change and loss through overgrazing, burning, afforestation and toxic chemicals are unclear. Merlins respond to disturbance by transferring their activities around the nest from open country to within the forest canopy. As a result they apparently tolerate a high level of disturbance outside the forest without adverse effect. The removal of Merlins for falconry (licenced or illegal), suspected of being a threat in some areas, is considered to be negligible (D. Norriss).

Conservation

The high Bezzel Index of 23 indicates the conservation significance of the Merlin.

Research programmes in the Republic (National Parks and Wildlife Service) and Northern Ireland (Royal Society for the Protection of Birds) have examined aspects of the population ecology of the Merlin and its conservation needs in selected areas. However, no specific conservation measures have been effected to date. There is now a need for a comprehensive national study of the species on its breeding grounds and throughout Ireland outside the breeding season and the protection of its main breeding and feeding areas. Blanket afforestation in Merlin habitat should be discontinued because it removes the hunting habitat. However, the planting of small, well dispersed conifer plantations could favour the Merlin (D. Norriss) in some specific localities.

CAPERCAILLIE

Tetrao urogallus

Extinct

RSPB/C. Palmar

Most writers on Irish ornithology have assumed that a well known Irish bird called the 'Cock of the Wood', which became extinct in the 18th century, was the Capercaillie. This view has been supported by Hall (1981) after a detailed examination of the literature, following a suggestion by Deane (1979) that the species never occurred in Ireland. The Capercaillie is a large, dark, grouse-like bird weighing up to 6.5kg. It is essentially a bird of mature coniferous forest but will also live in broadleaved woodland habitat (Cramp and Simmons 1980). Its main food consists of pine needles and shoots and a variety of other plant material such as Cranberry (Batten *et al*. 1990). The species is declining throughout Europe primarily as a result of habitat loss and shooting pressure.

LEG STATUS IRL	RoI Protected	**LEG STATUS EUR**	Birds Dir	I
	NI Protected		Bern	III
INTL LEG STATUS			Bonn	–
OCCURRENCE IN IRELAND	–	**BEZZEL INDEX, IRELAND**		–
BREEDING PAIRS	–	**WINTERING NUMBERS**		–

MAIN FOOD Pine needles and shoots, Bilberry, Cranberry, sedges

History of the Species in Ireland

At least eight 17th century sources refer to the Cock of the Wood as an Irish bird (Hall 1981). Thomas Comber (1778, cited by Hall 1981) wrote that when in 1637 Wandesforde acquired the estate of Castlecomer, Kilkenny, 'this princely estate abounded with all sorts of wildfowl, particularly a most stately bird never known in England, called the Cock of the Wood, as large as a Turky-cock, with black feathers, scarlet eyes and flesh more white and delicate than a Turky's; a rarity even in Ireland'. In 1711 the Irish Parliament passed 'An Act for the better Preservation of the Game' (11 Anne, c.7) which recognised the imminent risk of extinction of the species and provided protection for the birds, their nests and eggs. Thomas Pennant, who toured Ireland in 1754, believed that the species was extinct in Ireland by 1766 (Pennant 1766, cited by Hall 1981). The eminent 17th century zoologists Willughby and Ray (1678) also wrote of the existence of the Cock of the Wood in Ireland.

Current Distribution and Status

Palaearctic. The Capercaillie breeds predominantly in the boreal and temperate forest zone of the former USSR (north of 52°N) and Fenno-Scandia. In southern and western Europe there are smaller populations in the Alps, the Pyrenees, through former Yugoslavia to Albania, Bulgaria and former Czechoslovakia, and in Scotland. It occupies a range of woodland types including dense spruce and fir forests, more open taiga and pine/larch forests, mixed forests with birch and aspen, and stunted oak or mature oak woodlands. The Capercaillie prefers areas where woodland is broken by open terrain such as boggy dwarf heath with berried plants such as Bilberry. The species has declined, in some cases dramatically, throughout its range (Cramp and Simmons 1980).

In Scotland the Capercaillie inhabits mature open pinewoods with a shrubby understory of Bilberry, heather and Juniper. The species became extinct in about 1770 and was successfully re-introduced in 1837–38. The Scottish population is now believed to be between 1,000 and 2,000 individuals and has declined since the late 1960s (Batten *et al.* 1990).

Threats

Loss of habitat through felling of old Scots Pine forest, over-shooting and adverse climatic conditions, are blamed for the bird's decline in Scotland (Batten *et al.* 1990). Habitat destruction, shooting and human pressures are also responsible for its decline throughout its European range. In some countries (Germany, Spain) the hunting of Capercaillie is now banned.

Conservation

No thought has been given to the possibility of re-introducing Capercaillie to Ireland but it would be worth examining the feasibility of re-creating suitable habitat to facilitate this.

GREY PARTRIDGE

Perdix perdix **Endangered**

RSPB/D. Green

The native Grey Partridge is now an extremely scarce species in Ireland. It is resident and sedentary and has a preference for open arable farmland with hedgerows. However, in the seven counties where wild birds definitely still exist, grassland is important in Galway, cutaway bogland and bogland edge in Kildare, Offaly and Louth and mixed farmland with cereals and tillage in Tipperary, Wicklow and Wexford (Kavanagh 1991). The population decline in Ireland is part of a worldwide trend. The specific reasons for the decline in Ireland are not known but are likely to be related to the reduction in cereal growing, the removal of hedgerows and the use of pesticides and herbicides which has reduced the abundance of weed species and their associated insect fauna which, in turn, has led to lower chick survival. The Grey Partridge is at the edge of its range in Ireland so it is possible that climatic factors could also be implicated, directly or indirectly, in its demise.

LEG STATUS IRL	RoI Quarry	**LEG STATUS EUR**	Birds Dir	II/1,III/1
	NI Protected		Bern	III
INTL LEG STATUS			Bonn	–
OCCURRENCE IN IRELAND	R	**BEZZEL INDEX, IRELAND**		9(B)
BREEDING PAIRS	c 200	**WINTERING NUMBERS**		< 1,000 birds

MAIN FOOD Grasses, cereals, clovers, grain & weed seeds, insects

History of the Species in Ireland

In the nineteenth century the Grey Partridge bred in every county but by 1900 it was declining because of a reduction in wheat growing and an increase in shooting pressure. This decline accelerated during the first two decades of this century and the species would probably have become extinct had protective legislation and new stocks not been introduced in 1930 (Hutchinson 1989). The population increased again and coveys could even be found in such isolated districts as Carraroe in west Galway (Kennedy *et al.* 1954). However, a further decline set in in the 1960s and by 1968–72 it was proved breeding in only 180 10km squares, probably breeding in 26 and possibly in 48 (Sharrock 1976). By the early 1980s birds were restricted almost completely to the midlands with a few outlying populations in the north, east and south-east (28 10km squares; Lack 1986), although the winter population was probably under-recorded. Those remaining in Northern Ireland are almost certainly released birds (J.S. Furphy cited by Hutchinson 1989).

Current Distribution and Status

Palaearctic and introduced into northern North America. The Grey Partridge is resident throughout most of Britain and continental Europe south to northern Spain and Portugal, central Italy and Greece and locally in southern Norway, southern Sweden and Finland. The British breeding population may be 200,000–500,000 pairs including released birds. Recent population data are not available for the rest of Europe.

In Ireland it is now very locally distributed in small numbers. It was recorded in only thirty six 10km squares during the 1988–90 period of the New Breeding Atlas survey. It was confirmed or probably breeding in Louth, Mayo, Galway, Offaly, Kildare, Wicklow, Limerick, Tipperary and Wexford and reported in Antrim, Down, Tyrone, Donegal, Dublin and Cork (Gibbons *et al.* in press). However, wild Grey Partridges probably breed only in the seven counties mentioned in the introduction above, so it is likely that birds recorded elsewhere were of hand-reared stock. While the two surveys (Gibbons *et al.* in press; Kavanagh 1991) probably under-estimate its numbers and distribution (there may be upwards of 200 pairs [excluding released birds] left – B.P. Kavanagh) it seems clear that the indigenous population of Grey Partridges is very close to extinction in Ireland, a view shared by the National Association of Regional Game Councils (NARGC) (J. Dunne).

Small numbers of Grey Partridges have been released at two sites in Wexford and at one site in each of Longford and Laois. As part of a three year release programme in Wexford over 800 birds were released in 1989 and over 1,000 in 1990 (NARGC Annual Report 1989–90 and 1990–91). It is reported that some of the birds released in 1989 survived to breed (NARGC Annual Report 1990–91) and that about 200 of the birds released in 1990 survived (B.P. Kavanagh). It is reported that 1,500 birds are released annually in

Longford and that a couple of hundred birds are supplied from the same source to four or five other shoots, one of which is in Laois. There is no information on the survival of these birds in the wild (B.P. Kavanagh).

The Grey Partridge is declining worldwide and probably in all 31 countries in which it is found. It has declined by 80% since 1952 in Britain, contracted its range southwards in Scandinavia by 320km and almost disappeared from Norway. Its range is shrinking in Spain and Portugal and numbers are declining in Italy and France (Potts 1986). Some of the earliest and most dramatic declines, however, were in Ireland. The species was regarded as 'plentiful' in the seventeenth century by the Duke of Ormonde and large bags were achieved in Kildare up to the end of the nineteenth century. However, the decline alluded to earlier indicates to Potts (1986) that 'the [Grey] Partridge may soon be extinct in Ireland', a prophecy which has been borne out by the results of recent surveys.

Threats

The remaining Grey Partridge populations are likely to be threatened by reduction in habitat, intensification of pesticide and herbicide use, increased predation, continued shooting of the remaining natural population and possibly climatic change.

Conservation

Studies have been initiated on the remaining populations of Grey Partridge. Conservation measures implemented so far are: a total ban on shooting in Northern Ireland and restriction of shooting to the period 1–15 November in the Republic. Shooting should now be restricted to released populations only. The immediate conservation needs include the protection and management of the principal populations and their habitats and changes in agricultural policy (e.g., through Common Agricultural Policy reform) which will encourage the restoration of Grey Partridge habitat. This should include the use of Set Aside, the implementation of ESA schemes in appropriate areas and the trial introduction of pesticide/herbicide-free headlands in cereal-growing areas.

CORNCRAKE

Crex crex

Endangered

R.T. Mills

The Corncrake is a rapidly declining summer visitor and the only extant Irish bird listed as 'Rare' on a worldwide scale by the IUCN (IUCN 1990). Primarily it nests in hay meadows, but some birds nest in silage fields, rough pasture and, less frequently, in marshes, peat bogs, gardens, cereals and rootcrops (Mayes and Stowe 1989).

The demise of the Corncrake has resulted from the loss of nesting habitat and the destruction of females, nests and young caused by the mechanisation of hay cutting, early hay cutting and, during the past twenty years, the cutting of silage instead of hay. The conversion of hay meadows to sheep pasture in Fermanagh and Donegal has also reduced available habitat (R.A. Brown). Secondary factors likely to have affected the Corncrake population, mainly on migration, are collisions with overhead wires, lighthouses and other structures and trapping, especially in Egypt during Quail netting (Williams *et al.* 1991).

LEG STATUS IRL	RoI Protected	**LEG STATUS EUR**	Birds Dir	I
	NI Protected		Bern	II
INTL LEG STATUS	IUCN R		Bonn	–
OCCURRENCE IN IRELAND	S	**BEZZEL INDEX, IRELAND**		17(B)
BREEDING PAIRS	<250	**WINTERING NUMBERS**		None
MAIN FOOD	Invertebrates and seeds			

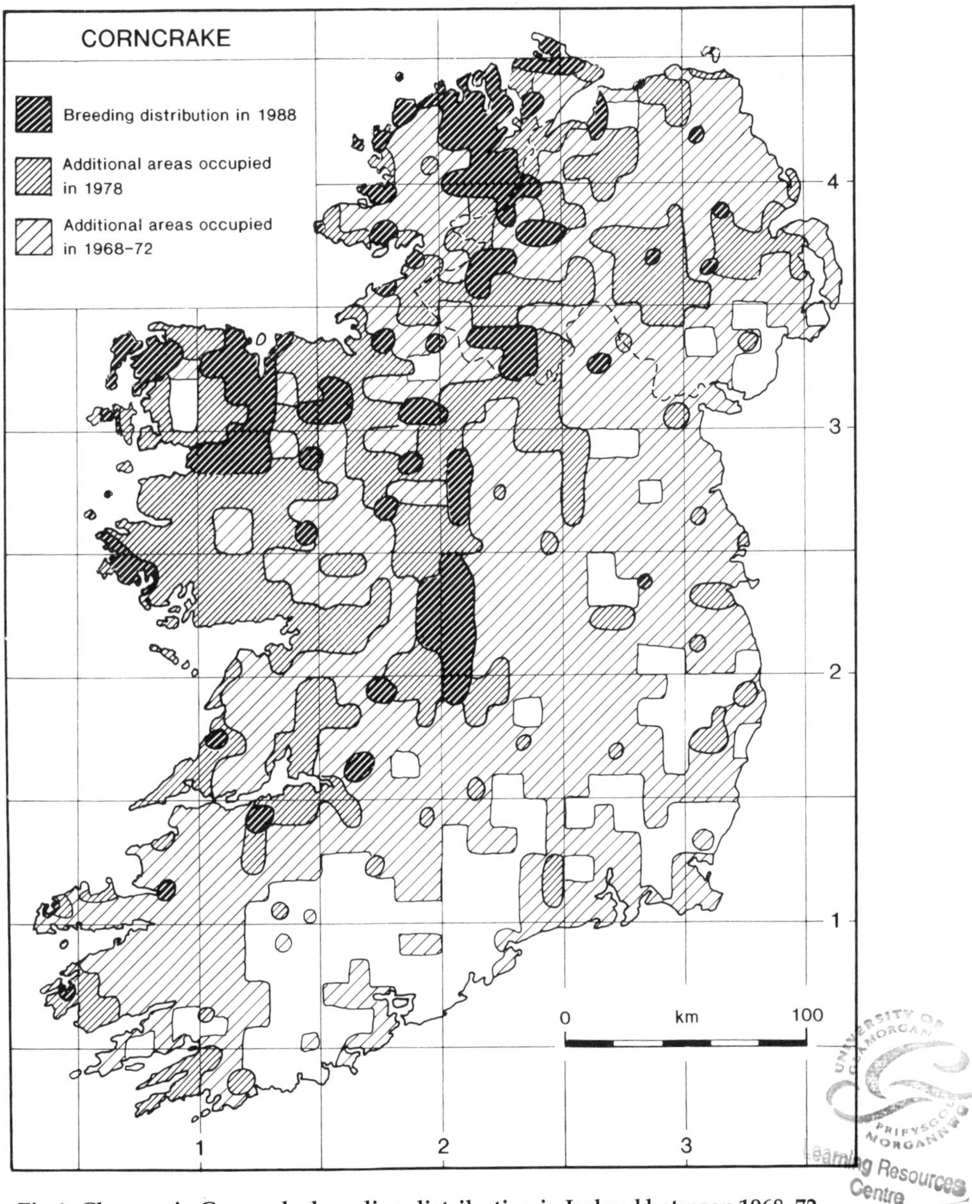

Fig 4 Changes in Corncrake breeding distribution in Ireland between 1968–72 and 1988 (based on Sharrock 1976; O'Meara 1979; and Mayes and Stowe 1989)

History of the Species in Ireland

During the first half of the eighteenth century the Corncrake is said to have been very numerous and fifty years later it was described as common in the north of Ireland. It was still breeding in every county at the end of the nineteenth century (O'Meara 1979) but in the early years of the twentieth the population started to decline and has continued to do so to the present day. In 1968–72 it was still breeding in all counties but densities were much lower than recorded in the 1930s (Hutchinson 1989). The decline accelerated during the 1970s and the population in 1978 was down to an estimated 1,200–1,500 pairs (Mayes and Stowe 1989) and concentrated mainly to the west of the River Shannon. A sample survey of seven important Corncrake habitats between 1978 and 1985 confirmed a continuing decline (O'Meara 1986) and a comprehensive survey in 1988 indicated that the total population had declined to 903–930 calling birds in a further contracted range (Mayes and Stowe 1989)(Figure 4). Sample counts in the Republic in 1989 and 1990 suggest that the decline is continuing (E. Mayes). In Northern Ireland only 45 calling birds were recorded in 1990 compared with 122–134 in 1988.

Current Distribution and Status

Palaearctic. The Corncrake formerly bred over much of northern and central Europe between 44°N and 63°N, extending to Siberia, 120°E, but the distribution is now much restricted and fragmented. It winters in south-eastern Africa (Batten *et al.* 1990). In Britain the population started declining and the range contracting in the late nineteenth century and now the species breeds only in north and west Scotland where 550–600 pairs were estimated in 1988 (Batten *et al.* 1990). The size of the population elsewhere in Europe is probably 3,000–4,000 pairs, of which 2,000 are in France (Stowe and Hudson 1988).

In Ireland the Corncrake is now confined mainly to the Shannon valley, the area west of the River Shannon and to the north-west. In 1988 the most densely populated areas were in north Donegal, the Moy catchment area in north Mayo, the islands of Inishturk and Inishbofin (off Mayo and Galway respectively), the Shannon callows between Athlone and Portumna and the area around Lough Erne in Fermanagh (Mayes and Stowe 1989). The numbers of Corncrakes recorded in 1988 are presented in Table 6. In 1989, 1990, 1991, 1992 and 1993 substantially fewer birds were heard calling in most counties. The Northern Ireland population declined to about 45 calling birds in 1990 (Williams *et al.* 1991) 21 in 1991, 15 in 1992 (RSPB) and 5 in 1993 (J.R. Sheppard). A preliminary analysis of the 1993 Corncrake survey indicated that the number of calling birds was down to 39–59 in the north-west, 64–65 in the west coast and 51 in the north midlands, giving a complete Irish total of approximately 159 to 171 breeding pairs (J.R. Sheppard, IWC/RSPB).

Threats

In Ireland, the continuing threats to the survival of the Corncrake are the intensification of grass management and the continuing abandonment of traditionally managed hay meadows. Other, secondary threats include collision (e.g. with barbed wire fences), predation by feral Domestic Cats and feral Mink, and human disturbance.

Turraun Bog, Co. Offaly.
Natural regeneration on a Bord na Mona cut over bog which provides one of the last refuges for Grey Partridge in Ireland. Nightjar also use bog margins. *(Photo: B. Kavanagh).*

Rockabill, Co. Dublin.
Rockabill, off the Dublin coast, supports Europe's largest colony of Roseate Terns. *(Photo: M. O Briain).*

Gortahork, Co. Donegal.
Traditional coastal small-holding showing small-scale mixed farming with unimproved grazing, potatoes, cereals, and hay as winter fodder. Habitat mixes such as this, which support Corncrake and Corn Bunting, are fast disappearing. *(Photo: The Slide File).*

Lough Beagh, Co. Donegal.
Upland lakes and lochans in the north-west support populations of Arctic Charr and Red-throated Diver. *(Photo: E. Mayes).*

Natterjack Toad habitat, Co. Kerry.
Coastal sand-dune lakes in Kerry which support Natterjack Toads are under threat from recreational development, agricultural pollution and drainage. *(Photo: R. T. Mills).*

Lough Beg ASSI, Co. Londonderry.
Much of the marshy grassland around lakes in Ireland has been lost through drainage and flood control. At the Lough Beg/Lough Neagh Ramsar Site this habitat is used by breeding Dunlin while the lough shore supports nesting Shoveler and Pochard.
(Photo: J. K. Partridge).

Natterer's Bat roost, Co. Down.
Derelict and disused buildings often provide vital roost sites for bats and Barn Owls. Many sites have been lost as buildings disintegrate, are demolished or unsympathetically renovated. *(Photo: J. K. Partridge).*

Stone-built bridge, Co. Galway.
Crevices on the undersides of stone bridges provide important roost sites for bats. This bridge has been sealed with concrete resulting in the loss of roost sites.
(Photo: C. M. McAney).

TABLE 6 Numbers of calling Corncrakes recorded in 1988 (Mayes and Stowe 1989)

Antrim	3	Down	1	Laois	4	Roscommon	56
Armagh	11	Dublin	2	Leitrim	9	Sligo	30–32
Cavan	1	Fermanagh	65–73	Limerick	3	Tipperary	2
Clare	12	Galway	63	Longford	6	Tyrone	26–28
Cork	6	Kerry	18	Mayo	163	Westmeath	10
Londonderry	11–13	Kildare	4–5	Monaghan	2	Wexford	1
Donegal	310–320	Kilkenny	1	Offaly	77–79	Wicklow	1

Conservation

Surveys and studies carried out in the Republic over the past two decades have provided a basis for conservation action in the 1990s. In 1991 a programme of survey and advice to farmers with Corncrakes on their land was undertaken by the Irish Wildbird Conservancy and the National Parks and Wildlife Service in conjunction with the Royal Society for the Protection of Birds. An Environmentally Sensitive Area in west Galway, designated in 1991, encompasses one breeding site.

In Northern Ireland a survey in 1990/91 to locate breeding Corncrakes in Fermanagh was followed up with financial compensation (from the Department of Environment for Northern Ireland) for farmers with Corncrakes on their land who are prepared to delay hay or silage cutting and to cut grass in a Corncrake-friendly manner.

In future consideration will be given to expanding and refining the schemes in the Republic and Northern Ireland, increasing state compensation payments to farmers and including more Corncrake breeding areas in Environmentally Sensitive Areas. The RSPB is also promoting a 'Hay Premium Scheme' through the EC Commission and national Agriculture Departments to encourage farmers in Corncrake breeding areas to revert from silage making to hay production (Williams *et al.* 1991).

GOLDEN PLOVER

Pluvialis apricaria **Vulnerable**

RSPB/D. Green

The Golden Plover is a scarce breeding bird but numerous in Ireland in the winter. It nests on mountain tops, wet blanket bogs, cut-over blanket bogs and occasionally on coastal machair (Nairn and Sheppard 1985). It is also associated with active turf cutting, recently burnt areas and where grazing is intense on blanket bogs in Connemara (H.J. Wilson). In winter it occurs on wet grassland, callows, turloughs and on the coast.

Historically it had a restricted distribution and a relatively small breeding population in Ireland which is at the south-western edge of its range. Climatic amelioration may have influenced its distribution in the past (Sharrock 1976). However, afforestation, over-grazing, burning and intensive turf exploitation have reduced the habitat available to it. Predators such as Hooded Crows, which are common in the west of Ireland, may also have had an adverse impact on the Golden Plover population.

LEG STATUS IRL	RoI	Quarry	**LEG STATUS EUR**	Birds Dir	I,II/2,III,3
	NI	Quarry		Bern	III
INTL LEG STATUS				Bonn	II
OCCURRENCE IN IRELAND	S,W,P,[R]		**BEZZEL INDEX, IRELAND**		17(B),13(W)
BREEDING PAIRS	c 300		**WINTERING NUMBERS**		200,000+

MAIN FOOD Invertebrates, berries, seeds and grasses

History of the Species in Ireland

It is probable that the Golden Plover was more common as a breeding species in the nineteenth century than it is today (Kennedy *et al.* 1954). It had abandoned all but the western and far northern counties by the middle of this century. However, it has sometimes been seen in recent years on top of Mangerton Mountain in Kerry in summer, but breeding has not been proved (T.D. Carruthers). The total population in the 1968–72 period was estimated to be about 600 pairs (Sharrock 1976) – possibly an overestimate. Eighteen pairs were located in Antrim in 1976 and Ennis (cited by Hutchinson 1989) considered that there were no more than 25 pairs breeding in that county. A survey in 1986 located 12 pairs in Antrim, 5 pairs in Tyrone and 25 pairs in Fermanagh (Partridge 1988a) and it was suggested that the total population in Northern Ireland at that time was less than 50 pairs (Partridge 1988b). In 1985 and 1986 Haworth (1987) located 28 and 41 occupied territories respectively in Connemara. There appear to be no quantitative estimates for the populations in Mayo, Sligo or Donegal.

Current Distribution and Status

The Golden Plover breeds in the north Palaearctic and winters in Ireland, Britain, the Netherlands, Belgium, France, locally in Spain, Italy, Greece, north Africa and south-west Asia. As a breeding bird it has decreased in Britain (since 1950), in Germany (25 pairs), Denmark (10 pairs) and Sweden (27,000–32,000 pairs) but increased in Finland between 1941 and 1976 (Cramp and Simmons 1983; Piersma 1986). The Norwegian population is 130,000 pairs (Batten *et al.* 1990). The European breeding population (outside Iceland and Fenno-Scandia) is about 23,000 pairs of which 22,700 are nesting in Britain (Stroud *et al.* 1987). In winter there are 750,000–1,000,000 in Europe.

In Ireland it is now restricted as a breeding species to the blanket bogs and mountains of Antrim, Tyrone, Fermanagh, Donegal, Leitrim, Sligo, Mayo, Galway and Kerry where it is estimated that there are no more than 300 pairs. During the 1988–90 period of the New Breeding Atlas survey Golden Plover were also recorded in Londonderry, Kildare, Laois, Clare, Cork and Wexford (Gibbons *et al.* in press). A pair nested in Waterford in 1991 but later abandoned the nest, one of the pair probably having been killed by a Peregrine (K. Preston).

The breeding birds are of the nominate race *P. a. apricaria* which breeds in Ireland, Britain and around the Baltic. The race *P. a. albifrons* breeds in Iceland, northern Europe and northern Siberia (Hutchinson 1989). Both races move south after breeding and the large winter population in Ireland is likely to be a mixture of the races (Cramp and Simmons 1983). It is not known whether any of the locally breeding birds remain in Ireland during the winter. Golden Plovers are widely distributed, mainly in the southern half of the country in winter (Lack 1986) on inland and coastal wetlands. The wintering population of over 200,000 birds is internationally important, being about 30% of the west European total (Batten *et al.* 1990).

Threats

Habitat destruction and disturbance (Yalden and Yalden 1989) by afforestation, over-grazing, burning, intensive turf cutting and predation present continuing threats to breeding Golden Plover in Ireland. The continued drainage of wet grassland poses a threat to the wintering population.

Conservation

In Northern Ireland several breeding sites are within existing and proposed Areas of Special Scientific Interest, Forest Nature Reserves and a Royal Society for the Protection of Birds Reserve. In the Republic several blanket bog breeding sites are protected. However, there is an urgent need for a comprehensive survey of the breeding population and its habitat and for the protection and management of areas not already in state ownership.

DUNLIN

Calidris alpina

Vulnerable

INP/R.H. Thompson

The Dunlin is a scarce breeding wader but occurs in large numbers, mainly on estuaries, during the winter and on spring and autumn passage. In the nesting season it is most frequently recorded on closely grazed, very wet and hummocky vegetation with plenty of pools and channels. It shows particular preference for damper sites with machair marsh vegetation (Nairn and Sheppard 1985). Inland it nests on callows near lakes and marshes (Hutchinson 1989), on blanket bogs and, at least until recently, on some lowland raised bogs. It is breeding at the south-western edge of the Palaearctic part of its range and, historically, has never been common in Ireland. Habitat destruction and disturbance are probably the main factors contributing to its decline.

LEG STATUS IRL	RoI Protected	LEG STATUS EUR	Birds Dir	–
	NI Protected		Bern	III
INTL LEG STATUS			Bonn	II
OCCURRENCE IN IRELAND	S,W,P,[R]	BEZZEL INDEX, IRELAND		19(B)
BREEDING PAIRS	< 300	WINTERING NUMBERS		100,000–150,000
MAIN FOOD	Invertebrates			

History of the Species in Ireland

The Dunlin was never numerous as a breeding species but is probably less widespread now than in the nineteenth century. During the 1968–72 period it was proved to breed in Londonderry, Tyrone, Fermanagh, Donegal, Mayo, Galway and Westmeath, probably breeding in Antrim, Longford and Clare and possibly breeding in Armagh, Sligo, Roscommon, Offaly and Laois (Sharrock 1976). The largest breeding concentration was on the Mullet in Mayo where up to 50 pairs were reported in the 1960s (Ruttledge 1966b). In 1985, in a survey of the breeding birds of west coast machair, there were 17 pairs in Donegal, 4 pairs in Sligo, 94 pairs in Mayo and 6 pairs in Galway (Nairn and Sheppard 1985). At this time the Mullet population held only 15 pairs (R.G.W. Nairn, cited by Hutchinson 1989) and by 1990 there were 'not many' pairs recorded here (R.A. Chapman). In 1986/87 Partridge (1988a) located 7 pairs at Lower Lough Erne, Fermanagh, and two pairs on upland sites and suggested that the total population in Northern Ireland numbered 10–20 pairs (J.K. Partridge).

Current Distribution and Status

Holarctic. The race *C. a. schinzii* breeds in Iceland, southern Scandinavia, Britain, Ireland and western Europe. About 9,150 pairs of *schinzii* breed in Britain out of a total of about 11,000 pairs in temperate Europe. About 300,000 pairs breed in Iceland (Piersma 1986).

In Ireland breeding Dunlin are confined to the north-western sector with the main concentration on or near the coasts of Donegal, Sligo, Mayo and Galway with some inland populations in Antrim, Fermanagh and Roscommon. Small numbers were present but not confirmed breeding in Down, Londonderry, Tyrone, Cavan, Longford, Dublin, Clare, Kerry, Cork and Waterford during the 1988–90 period of the New Breeding Atlas survey (Gibbons *et al.* in press).

Many of the summer and autumn passage migrants are of the race which breeds in Ireland (*C. a. schinzii*), but by mid-winter the race *C. a. alpina*, which breeds from northern Scandinavia eastwards, is predominant (Greenwood 1984) in the population of 100,000–150,000 birds. It is not known whether the locally breeding birds remain in Ireland during the winter.

Threats

Continued habitat destruction and disturbance by agricultural intensification are the main threats to breeding Dunlin.

Conservation

Small numbers of Dunlin breed in existing reserves on Lower Lough Erne, in Donegal and in Mayo. Otherwise no specific measures have been taken to conserve the species. In the absence of detailed information on the distribution and abundance of nesting birds there is an immediate need for a comprehensive survey of the breeding population and its habitats. It is also necessary that the known breeding habitats, in particular the west coast machair, be protected and managed for the benefit of breeding Dunlin.

BLACK-TAILED GODWIT

Limosa limosa **Rare**

INP/R.H. Thompson

The Black-tailed Godwit is a very rare breeding wader but a common winter visitor on estuaries and a passage migrant on estuaries and inland waters. The Shannon Estuary, the Little Brosna, Cork Harbour and Dungarvan Harbour are notable for large flocks outside the breeding season. Its breeding habitat is damp grassland and its favoured nesting sites are in fields which have been flooded in winter and grazed in spring. In Ireland it is breeding at the south-western edge of its range and although it has nested almost annually since 1975 it is likely that habitat conditions do not regularly meet its requirements.

LEG STATUS IRL	RoI Protected	LEG STATUS EUR	Birds Dir	II/2
	NI Protected		Bern	III
INTL LEG STATUS			Bonn	II
OCCURRENCE IN IRELAND	S,W,P	BEZZEL INDEX, IRELAND		17(B),17(W)
BREEDING PAIRS	2–4	WINTERING NUMBERS		8,000–10,000

MAIN FOOD Primarily invertebrates, some plant material

History of the Species in Ireland

The Black-tailed Godwit was first recorded breeding in 1975 and it has bred almost annually and in at least three counties since. One to two pairs have nested on the Shannon Callows at different sites in several years including 1985 (R.G.W. Nairn), 1986 (1 nest, I.J. Herbert), 1987 (2 pairs, Nairn *et al.* 1988), possibly in 1988 on the west side of the river, suspected in 1989 (R. Devlin) but not in 1990 (I.J. Herbert). Birds were seen displaying beside the Shannon north of Clonmacnoise in mid-May 1991 (H.J.Wilson). A pair nested unsuccessfully in Wexford in 1979. In another southern county breeding occurred from 1983 to 1986. Here at least two pairs bred in 1983, 1984 and 1986 and at least one pair in 1985 (Hutchinson 1989). Non-breeding summer visitors occur in the vicinity of Lough Beg, Londonderry and at Tacumshin Lake in Wexford (up to 150 birds).

Current Distribution and Status

Palaearctic. The Black-tailed Godwit breeds locally in Norway, Finland, Britain and France. Small populations breed in Sweden, Denmark, Belgium and Germany while the bulk of the European population nests in the Netherlands. The total European breeding population is 102,000 to 123,000 pairs (*L. l. limosa*) and 10,000–30,000 pairs (*L. l. islandica*). About 50 pairs breed in Britain.

In Ireland the species now seems to be confined to the Shannon callows between Athlone and Portumna where 1–2 pairs (suspected to be *L. l. islandica*) breed almost annually. During the 1988–90 period of the New Breeding Atlas survey birds were reported in the breeding season in Down, Mayo, Roscommon, Offaly and Laois but breeding was not confirmed (Gibbons *et al.* in press).

Threats

The main threats to breeding birds are flooding, the inappropriate timing of grassland management and duration of grazing, disturbance of its nesting sites and predation.

Conservation

The intermittent breeding of small numbers of birds, often at different locations from year to year, makes conservation management very difficult. However, it is important that monitoring of the breeding birds is undertaken on an annual basis and that known nesting areas are protected and managed for the benefit of breeding Black-tailed Godwits.

GREENSHANK

Tringa nebularia **Rare**

RSPB/D. Green

The Greenshank is a very rare and probably intermittent breeding wader and a scarce winter visitor and passage migrant on the coast and at some inland wetlands. Ireland supports a significant proportion of the small numbers which winter in Ireland and Britain (Sheppard in press; Kirby *et al.* 1990, 1991). Its breeding habitat is open blanket bog. Its scarcity is likely to be associated with the fact that Ireland is at the extreme south-western edge of its breeding range.

LEG STATUS IRL	RoI Protected	**LEG STATUS EUR**	Birds Dir	II/2
	NI Protected		Bern	III
INTL LEG STATUS			Bonn	II
OCCURRENCE IN IRELAND	[S],W,P	**BEZZEL INDEX, IRELAND**		22(B),25(W)
BREEDING PAIRS	1?	**WINTERING NUMBERS**		750–1,000
MAIN FOOD	Invertebrates and small fish			

History of the Species in Ireland

A pair of Greenshanks nested in Achill, Mayo, in 1972 and 1974, and probably in 1971 and 1973. One fledgling was seen in each of 1972 and 1974

(Ruttledge 1978a). Since then, breeding has not been confirmed but it is possible that occasional breeding pairs have escaped attention (Hutchinson 1989).

Current Distribution and Status

Palaearctic and wintering in southern Europe, Africa, southern Asia and Australia. The European breeding population of Greenshanks is confined to Norway (17,000 pairs), Sweden (50,000 pairs), Finland (40,000 pairs) (Piersma 1986) and Scotland (960 pairs). The Irish wintering population is significant within the EC and about 5% of the Eastern Atlantic Flyway population winters in Ireland (Stroud *et al.* 1990).

Birds were present during the breeding season in upland habitats in Fermanagh, Donegal, Sligo, Mayo and Kerry in 1989 and 1990 but there was no evidence of breeding (R.A. Chapman, D.C. Cotton, J. Hennigan). Birds have also been recorded in Kildare during the breeding season.

Ireland is important for passage migrant and wintering Greenshanks and the estimated total of 750–1,000 birds constitutes a large proportion of the Irish and British total. They are widely distributed around the coast, usually in small parties (1–20), in sheltered estuaries and bays.

Threats

None known.

Conservation

No conservation measures are required at present. However, routine recording of Greenshank throughout the year, and during the breeding season in nesting habitat in particular, is desirable.

RED-NECKED PHALAROPE

Phalaropus lobatus **Endangered**

INP/J. Malins

The Red-necked Phalarope is a very rare and now probably intermittent breeding species and a rare passage migrant. It breeds at sites with open water, emergent swamp and wet and dry mire. Open water is necessary for courtship and copulation and for some feeding (Batten *et al.* 1990). Its breeding site in Mayo is the most southerly in the world and thus on the edge of the species' range. Egg collecting contributed to the decline of the species in the 1920s and 1930s (O.J. Merne). Climatic factors may also have influenced the fortunes of the species in Ireland as may changing land management practices and disturbance.

LEG STATUS IRL	RoI Protected	**LEG STATUS EUR**	Birds Dir	I
	NI Protected		Bern	II
INTL LEG STATUS			Bonn	II
OCCURRENCE IN IRELAND	S,P	**BEZZEL INDEX, IRELAND**		22(B)
BREEDING PAIRS	1?	**WINTERING NUMBERS**		None (very rare vagrant)
MAIN FOOD	Invertebrates			

History of the Species in Ireland

The colony of Red-necked Phalaropes at Annagh, Mayo, was first found in 1900 when two or three pairs were seen on the marsh. Breeding was proved in 1902 and since then the colony has survived, though with varying success (Hutchinson 1989).

The Annagh colony grew rapidly to 50 pairs in 1905 and continued, presumably, at this high level through 1923 after which a decline set in as indicated in Table 7. During the years of high numbers two other sites, 5km and 8km respectively from Annagh, were colonized. Two or three pairs bred at the nearer colony in 1920 but none was present in 1924. A few pairs continued to breed intermittently at the further colony after 1924. In 1932 there were six pairs but by 1944 only one pair bred there. From 1950 to 1967 the Annagh colony comprised only one or two pairs but between 1967 and 1971 extra non-breeding birds appeared and the population peaked at five pairs. During this period several other areas were colonised in Galway, Wexford and Kerry (Ruttledge 1978b; King 1980) but breeding has not been reported at any of these sites since.

Current Distribution and Status

Holarctic and circumpolar. The Red-necked Phalarope breeds mainly within the tundra and sub-arctic zones. In Europe it breeds in Iceland, the Faeroes, northern Fenno-Scandia and very locally in northern Scotland. The European population is about 150,000 pairs of which up to 19 nest in Scotland and one in Ireland. The winter range is unknown but may be in the southern Atlantic off the west coast of equatorial Africa (Batten *et al.* 1990).

In Ireland the species must now be considered as an extremely rare, intermittent breeder at just one site in north-west Mayo.

Threats

Disturbance and inappropriate land management (drainage, fencing, lack of grazing) are likely to be the major local threats to the continued breeding of the Red-necked Phalarope in Mayo.

Conservation

Annagh Marsh is an Irish Wildbird Conservancy reserve. However, lack of resources prevents appropriate monitoring and management of the reserve and land developments adjacent to the marsh, which may adversely affect it, cannot be effectively controlled. The fact that birds sometimes nest and feed outside the reserve adds to management difficulties. If the reserve is to continue to attract and support breeding Red-necked Phalaropes, it must be expanded to take in all areas used by the birds and monitored every year throughout the breeding season. Appropriate management of the fields and ponds within the reserve and the removal of fencing will also be required (D. Allen).

TABLE 7 Breeding sites of Red-necked Phalarope (based on Kennedy et al. *1954, Ruttledge 1978b, King 1980, Ruttledge 1982, Hutchinson 1989)*

	ANNAGH, Mayo	OTHER SITES	
Year	**Number of pairs (+non-breeders)**	**Site**	**Number of pairs**
1900	2–3		
1902	Breeding proved		
1905	50		
1911/12		Dooaghtry, Mayo	Breeding
1919	20	5km from Annagh	2–3
		8km from Annagh	A few pairs
1923	40–50		
1924		5km from Annagh	0
		Roaninish, Donegal	1
1927		Roaninish, Donegal	1
1929		Roaninish, Donegal	1
1930–34		Murroe, Donegal	1
1932	13	8km from Annagh	6
1940	6		
1944	5	8km from Annagh	1
1945	2		
<1950	a few		
1953–66	1–4	Dooaghtry, Mayo (1953–56)	1
1967	1–2 (+8)	Turloughcor, Galway	1
1968	3–5 (+20)	Lady's Island Lake, Wexford	1 female
1969	3 (+8)	Akeragh Lough, Kerry	2
1970	5 (+20)	Glenamaddy, Galway	2–3
		Akeragh Lough, Kerry	2
1971	3–4 (+12)	Akeragh Lough, Kerry	1
		Lady's Is Lake, Wexfd	nest+3 eggs
1972	0 (+3)	Akeragh Lough, Kerry	1 bird
1973–78	0		
1974		Glenamaddy, Galway	3 birds
1976		Glenamaddy, Galway	1 bird
1979	1 (+3)		
1980	Bred		
'81–'90	0–2		
1989	1 (Breeding not confirmed)		
1990	1 (Breeding not confirmed)		
1991	1 individual (Breeding not confirmed)		
1992	1 individual (Breeding not confirmed)		
1993	1 (Breeding not confirmed)		

ROSEATE TERN

Sterna dougallii **Endangered**

R.T. Mills

The Roseate Tern is a rare breeding species, the numbers of which have fluctuated considerably during the past century in the European and North American part of its range for reasons which are not yet fully understood. It nests on small offshore islands and on islands in coastal lagoons with sheltered rocks and vegetation. In this context, Tree Mallow appears to provide an attractive habitat on Rockabill and at its colonies in Brittany (O.J. Merne). It usually nests amongst Common Terns and Arctic Terns.

The Roseate Tern is primarily a species of warmer climates and it is possible that climatic factors influence its distribution and status at the northern edge of its range in Europe. However, eggs and adults were collected at Rockabill in the mid-nineteenth century (O.J. Merne) and this persecution may have contributed to its decline in Ireland. Its subsequent population increase in Ireland and Britain coincided with the introduction of protective measures and with the warmer years of the first half of the twentieth century; the reversal of the trend corresponds with the current period of cooling.

More immediate causes of declines and re-distributions within Ireland and Britain included the disappearance of Tern Island from Wexford Harbour, the erosion of Green Island in Carlingford Lough (D. Allen) and possibly high levels of predation by mammals and gulls at sites such as Lady's Island Lake in Wexford and some of the Strangford Lough islands (Down) (Brown and McAvoy 1985). Competition for space with gulls is a problem suffered by several tern species and at some sites this could affect Roseate Terns.

The exploitation of Roseate Terns for food and sport in their African wintering areas is also considered to be a contributory factor (Everett *et al.* 1987).

LEG STATUS IRL	RoI Protected	LEG STATUS EUR	Birds Dir	I
	NI Protected		Bern	II
INTL LEG STATUS			Bonn	II
OCCURRENCE IN IRELAND	S	BEZZEL INDEX, IRELAND		26(B)
BREEDING PAIRS	c 503 (1993)	WINTERING NUMBERS		None
MAIN FOOD Marine fish				

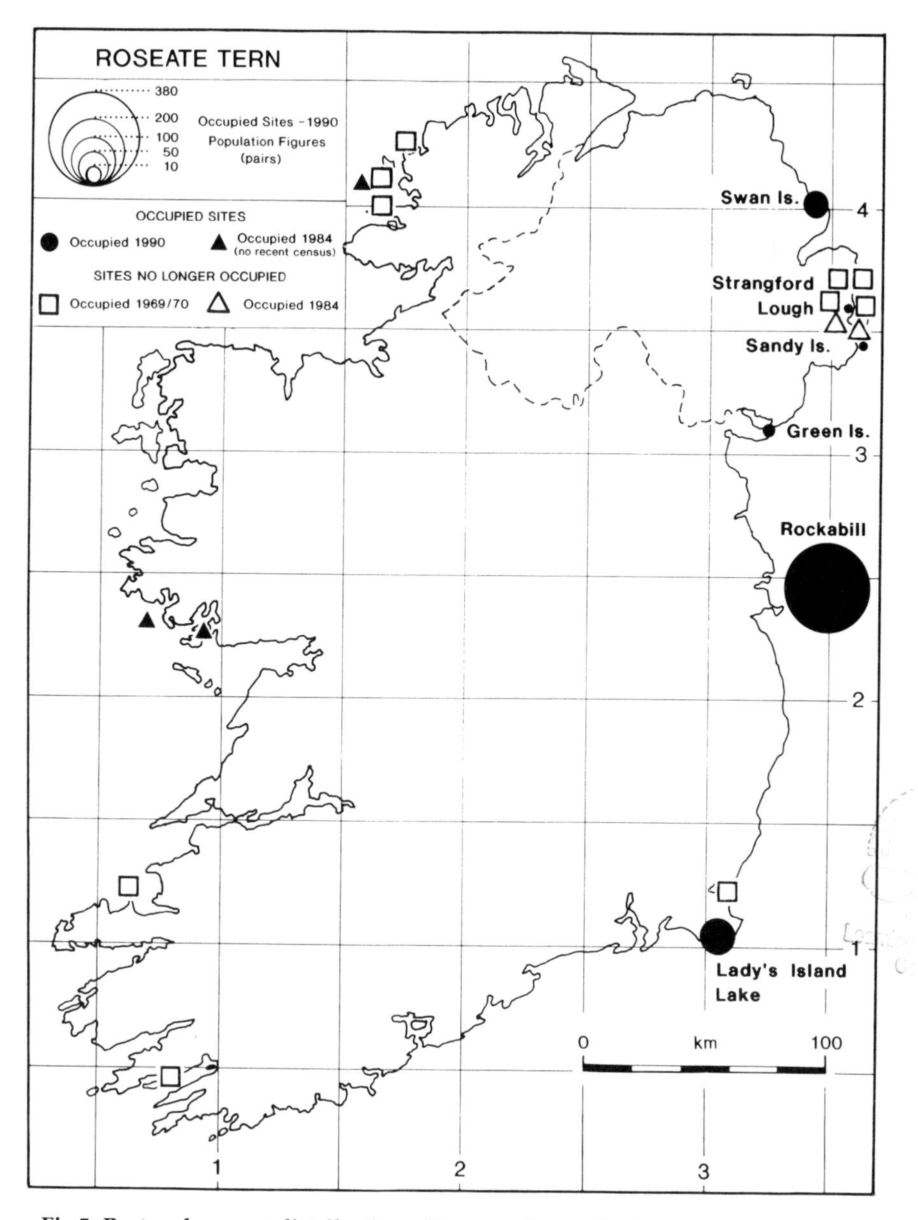

Fig 5 Past and present distribution of Roseate Tern colonies in Ireland (Based on Whilde 1985, Elliott 1991, Brown and McAvoy1985, and Merne 1974).

History of the Species in Ireland

Although only first recognised as a species in 1813 (Reid-Henry and Harrison 1988) it is reported that the Roseate Tern bred in considerable numbers in a few localities on the east coast of Ireland during the first half of the nineteenth century. Among the known breeding sites then were Mew Island off Down and Rockabill off Dublin where there was a 'very large colony' (hundreds) in 1844. It had become rare by 1865 and by 1900 it was very rare indeed, if not extinct as a breeding species. A few pairs returned in 1906 and in 1908 several pairs nested in Strangford Lough. In 1913 20–25 pairs were recorded at Malahide and the species appears to have nested there in small numbers (up to 20 pairs) in the 1920s and perhaps later (Kennedy *et al.* 1954, Hutchinson 1989).

The total population appears to have increased to a peak in the early 1960s when 2,000 pairs nested on Tern Island in Wexford Harbour. Subsequently, a decline set in in Ireland and accelerated through the 1970s bringing the population down to 268 pairs by 1984 (Whilde 1985). In recent years there has been a revival, the population rising to 323 pairs in 1987, to 406 pairs in 1990 and 426 pairs in 1991 (Figure 5).

It is likely that the population in Ireland and Britain peaked in the late 1950s and early 1960s at about 3,500 pairs, with probably well over 2,000 of these in Ireland. The Irish and British population declined to about 430 pairs in 1987 with only about 110 pairs at less than a dozen British sites. In 1988 the British total increased to about 136 pairs (Batten *et al.* 1990) bringing the Irish and British total up to about 470 pairs, a level maintained in 1989 and improved upon slightly in 1990 when the total reached 490 pairs. During the period 1988–90 the total European population remained at 1,500–1,600 pairs, of which about 1,000 pairs were on the Azores.

Current Distribution and Status

The Roseate Tern has a cosmopolitan but highly fragmented range. In Europe it breeds only very locally in Ireland, Britain, France (Brittany) and in the Azores (Portugal) which hold nearly two-thirds of the population (Figure 6). Ghana is the main early wintering area for the Irish and British birds (Gochfield 1983; Batten *et al.* 1990). The late winter distribution is not known.

The total world population is estimated at about 44,000 pairs, of which 75% are found in a broad belt from the Indian Ocean to south-east Asia, Australasia and some of the Pacific islands. About 15% breed in the tropics of the New World, centred around the Caribbean. The remaining 10% breed in Europe and on the east coast of the United States, the latter population accounting for two-thirds of the North Atlantic total (Everett *et al.* 1987, Elliott 1991).

In Ireland the great majority of the population now breeds at two sites, Rockabill – 427 pairs – and Lady's Island Lake – 76 pairs (IWC, 1993 figures) – with a diminishing balance nesting at a number of sites in north-east

Ireland and, perhaps, on some west coast islands. Since the demise of Tern Island, Wexford, in the mid-1970s there appears to have been considerable movement between colonies within Ireland and between Ireland and Anglesey, on the north-west coast of Wales, in particular. In 1989 there was a shift of birds from Rockabill to Anglesey (Avery and del Nevo 1990) but in 1990 the reverse seems to have been the case and of 88 non-Rockabill ringed birds seen on Rockabill 66 came from Anglesey (Cabot 1990). There appears to have been an almost total shift of birds from Strangford Lough where the population has declined from 156 in 1978 to 43 in 1985, none in 1987/88/89,

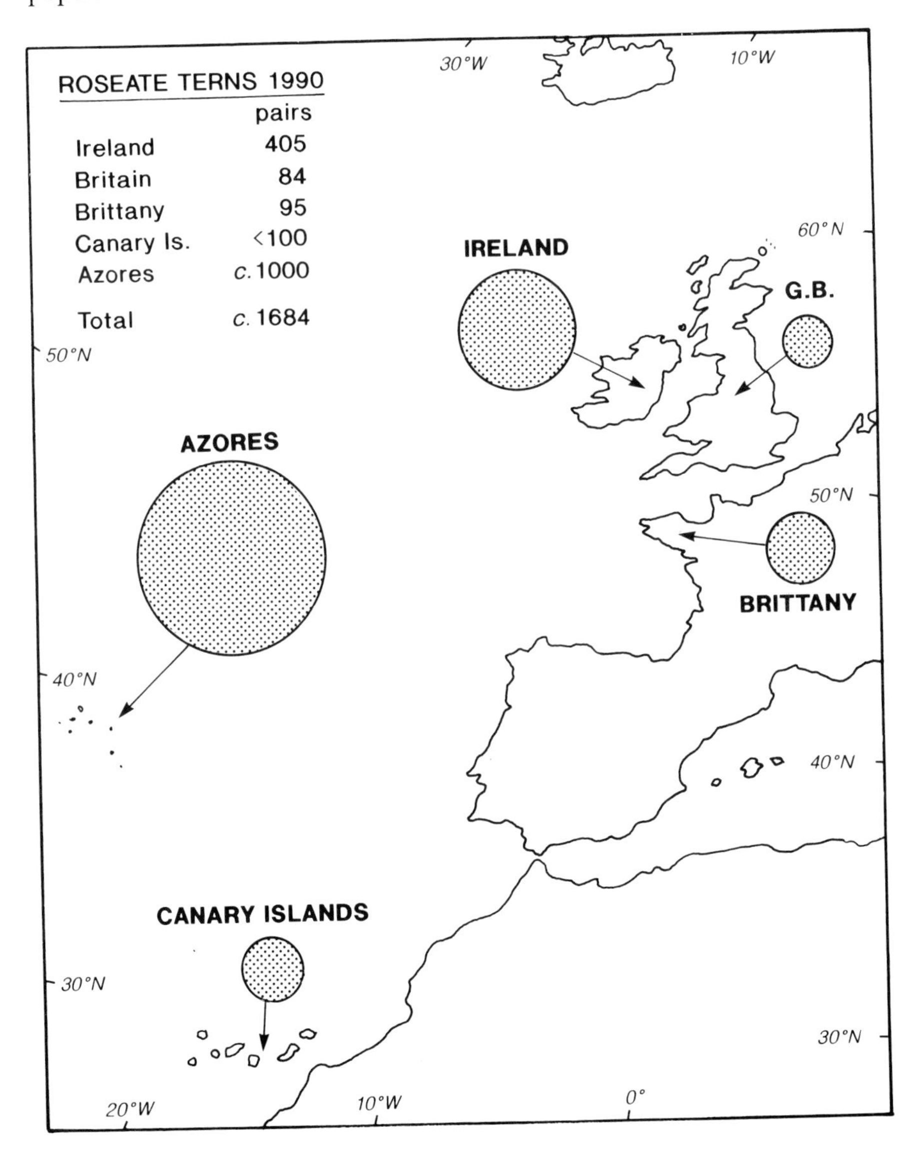

Fig 6 Distribution of Roseate Terns in the North-east Atlantic in 1990 (Based on Avery and del Nevo 1991 and Elliott 1991).

1 in 1990 and none in 1991. Roseate Terns have now virtually disappeared from the other Northern Ireland colonies; the Province held only two pairs in 1992 and none in 1993, although birds were present (D. Allen RSPB).

The Irish population accounts for about 25% of the European population (but about 65% if the Azores sub-population is discounted).

Threats

Predation by mammals such as Common Rats and birds such as the large gulls poses a threat to nesting Roseate Terns at several sites. The disappearance of suitable protective vegetation could deter nesting or expose birds to increased predation and disturbance on some islands. Flooding in storms poses an additional threat on some of the smaller, exposed islands, as does erosion of some of the less stable islands.

Conservation

Several of the islands used by Roseate Terns in Down and Antrim are Nature Reserves or other protected areas. On a number of these Common Rat and large gull control have been undertaken to the benefit of the nesting terns. Rockabill is a lighthouse island (owned by the Commissioners of Irish Lights) which was designated a statutory Refuge for Fauna in 1988 and is also a Special Protection Area under the EC 'Birds Directive'. Since the lighthouse went automatic a collaborative protection scheme between the Irish Wildbird Conservancy and the National Parks and Wildlife Service has undertaken wardening and the provision of nest boxes (250+ by 1992) on the island during the breeding season, culling gulls prior to the arrival of the terns, scaring gulls during the nesting period and the prevention of disturbance by human visitors. The Royal Society for the Protection of Birds provided expertise for this project with funding from RSPB, the Heritage Council and CIBA Geigy Ireland. Lady's Island Lake is a Statutory Refuge for Fauna and a Special Protection Area. The culling of large gulls and the control of Cats, Foxes, feral Mink and a Badger has led to an increase in numbers and breeding success of the terns nesting on Inish and Sgarbheen Islands.

The conservation of Roseate Terns in Ireland requires a continuation of the present monitoring, management and protection activities at the major colonies and routine surveys of other sites on the east coast to which the birds may move, and of sites on the west coast where very small numbers may nest.

LITTLE TERN

Sterna albifrons

Vulnerable

R.T. Mills

The Little Tern breeds in small numbers at about forty sites on the east, south and west coasts of Ireland. In 1984 about 50% nested on offshore islands and 50% on sandy and shingle beaches on the mainland coast (Whilde 1984). In Ireland the species is nesting at the northern edge of its range and climatic factors may be influencing its distribution. For example, it is suggested (Reid-Henry and Harrison 1988) that numbers peaked in Britain during the 1930s – a time of relative warmth. More immediate constraints on the population in Ireland are the limited availability of specialized nesting habitat which is free from human disturbance and predation by mammals and birds.

LEG STATUS IRL	RoI Protected	**LEG STATUS EUR**	Birds Dir	I
	NI Protected		Bern	II
INTL LEG STATUS			Bonn	–
OCCURRENCE IN IRELAND	S	**BEZZEL INDEX, IRELAND**		15(B)
BREEDING PAIRS	*c* 300	**WINTERING NUMBERS**		None
MAIN FOOD	Marine fish and crustaceans			

History of the Species in Ireland

Being widely dispersed in small colonies, often at inaccessible sites, the Little Tern is a difficult species to survey and enumerate. Historical records, therefore, are fragmentary and give little indication of population trends. The species may have been more numerous in the late nineteenth and early twentieth century for the climatic reasons indicated above. At the turn of the century there were a few colonies with upwards of 50 pairs (Ussher and Warren 1900) but by the 1950s it was exceptional to find more than 25 pairs in a colony (Kennedy *et al.* 1954). However, since Little Tern colonies fluctuate and shift from year to year it is unwise to suggest that the above observations indicate a trend.

In 1969–70 the total population was estimated to be at least 296 pairs (Cramp *et al.* 1974). A comprehensive survey in 1984 indicated 266 pairs. However, this was probably a minimum count because disturbance at several east coast colonies led to the movement of birds which may not have been counted subsequently. The population in 1984 was, therefore, more likely to have been around 300 and, it is considered, 10–20% smaller than in 1969–70 and, as Table 8 shows, substantially re-distributed.

Protection of several colonies on the east coast from 1986 onwards has led to an increase in breeding numbers and success. In 1984 there were 66–69 pairs in five colonies and by 1987 this had risen to 108 pairs in only two colonies (I.J. Herbert; Cooney 1987; Cooney *et al.* 1991; O Briain and Farrelly 1990). By 1992 six colonies were occupied but numbers had fallen to 73–78 pairs (Farrelly 1992).

Whether the population increases recorded during the early years of colony protection indicated real increases or merely a concentration of the population at the protected sites is not known, though the latter interpretation seems the more plausible. However, even if the latter is the case, an improved pool of new terns will be available to enter subsequent breeding populations (O Briain and Farrelly 1990) except from years such as 1990 and 1991 when productivity was low.

TABLE 8 Comparison of county totals (pairs) of Little Terns in 1969-70 and 1984

County	1969–70	1984
Louth	not counted	36
Dublin	13	15
Wicklow	50	15
Wexford	100	45
Cork	2	2
Kerry	11	10
Galway	60	45
Mayo	12	80
Sligo	2	—
Donegal	40	18
Londonderry	6	—
Total	**296**	**266**

Current Distribution and Status

The Little Tern has a world-wide distribution and breeds throughout temperate Europe, in parts of northern Mediterranean and in West Africa, Asia, Australia and North America. Within Europe breeding occurs mainly in Britain, France, Spain, the Netherlands, Germany, Italy, Greece, Denmark, Sweden and Finland (colonized in 1960). There has been a decline in numbers across most of this range in the second half of the twentieth century and the current population in western Europe is 5,000–5,500 pairs (Batten *et al.* 1990).

In Ireland the population is probably about 300 pairs, which represents 2.3% of the EC population.

Threats

Predation and disturbance will continue to be major threats at many Little Tern nesting sites, particularly on the east coast. The predators of most concern are Common Rats, Foxes, Stoats and Hooded Crows, but Hedgehogs and Kestrels may also have significant local effects. Flooding at high tides and heavy rain flooding dune slacks also pose threats to some colonies.

Conservation

Little Tern breeding sites are protected at North Bull Island in Dublin, The Raven and Bar o'Lough (Ballyteigue Burrow) in Wexford, which are National Nature Reserves, and at Lady's Island Lake which is a Statutory Refuge for Fauna. North Bull Island, Lady's Island Lake and the Inishkea Islands are designated as Special Protection Areas under the EC 'Birds Directive'. From 1986–1992 the Irish Wildbird Conservancy undertook voluntary wardening activities at North Bull Island (Dublin) and Kilcoole (Wicklow) with the results mentioned earlier and at Big Burrow, Cahore Point (Wexford), Portrane (Dublin), Portmarnock (Dublin) and the Boyne Estuary (Louth/Meath) in the earlier years of the period (I.J. Herbert). The National Parks and Wildlife Service of the Office of Public Works has assisted this work and undertaken protection work at The Raven (Wexford).

A repeat of the 1984 All Ireland Survey is planned and continued monitoring of the Tern population will be required thereafter. Continued protection of east coast sites is desirable as is the establishment of similar schemes on Inishmaan and Inishmore off the Galway coast and possibly at other west coast sites.

BARN OWL

Tyto alba

Indeterminate

RSPB/R.T. Smith

The Barn Owl is a resident species, breeding over much of the country but apparently absent from parts of the west (Sharrock 1976; Gibbons *et al.* in press). It roosts and nests mainly in buildings and trees and prefers open or lightly wooded country, including recently established conifer plantations for feeding. However, several pairs have also bred within and on the outskirts of Waterford City (Walsh and McGrath 1988). Most Barn Owls breed below an elevation of 100m (150m in the milder west) and where snow cover is of short duration (Shawyer 1987).

In Ireland the most important prey items are Wood Mice, Common Rats and, where available in the south-west, Bank Voles (Fairley and Smal 1989, Smal 1987). Also taken are Pygmy Shrews, a range of birds, bats, Common Frogs and, in urban habitats, House Mice (Fairley and Smal 1989, Walsh 1984).

The relative scarcity of Barn Owls in Ireland can be attributed primarily to an unfavourable climate because the species is poorly adapted to wet, cool conditions. It is primarily a tropical/sub-tropical species and it is at the extremity of its natural range in Ireland (C.M. Smal). Lack of diversity and numbers of small mammals (exacerbated by the use of rodenticides and improved management of on-farm grain storage), loss of nesting habitat, disappearance and fragmentation of foraging habitat, secondary poisoning from rodenticides and lack of suitable woodland breeding sites have also contributed to its scarcity (C.M. Smal).

LEG STATUS IRL	RoI Protected	**LEG STATUS EUR**	Birds Dir	I
	NI Protected		Bern	II
INTL LEG STATUS			Bonn	–
OCCURRENCE IN IRELAND	R	**BEZZEL INDEX, IRELAND**		10(B)
BREEDING PAIRS	600–900?	**WINTERING NUMBERS**		1,200–1,400?
MAIN FOOD	Small mammals and some small birds			

History of the Species in Ireland

Although never numerous the Barn Owl is reported to have bred in every county in the early part of the nineteenth century. It was even recorded breeding on remote islands such as Rathlin (Antrim), the Arān Islands (Galway) and Inishkeel off Donegal (Kennedy *et al.* 1954). A decrease was noted from the 1950s onwards and after 1960 the species disappeared from many of its former haunts (Ruttledge 1966b). The 1968–72 breeding survey (Sharrock 1976) indicates that it was most common in the south-west, in a band stretching from Clare to Dublin, and northwards from Dublin along the coastal strip into Northern Ireland. Elsewhere it was thinly distributed and entirely absent from most of west Galway, west Mayo, west Donegal, much of Cork and the offshore islands. At this time the population, using a conservative estimate of four pairs per occupied 10km square (Sharrock 1976), might have been in the order of 1,000 pairs. By 1982–85 it was estimated from a sample survey that the population was 600–900 pairs (Shawyer 1987*). During the same period in part of Armagh – where 14 nest sites had been recorded in the mid-1960s – birds were found nesting at only eight locations in 1982–83 and one in 1984. No nest sites were found in that area after 1984 (C. Dawson cited by Hutchinson 1989).

Current Distribution and Status

Cosmopolitan. The Barn Owl is said to be the most widespread land bird in the world with a mainly tropical and sub-tropical distribution between latitudes 40°N and 40°S (Batten *et al.* 1990). It is represented worldwide by a number of sub-species (C.M. Smal). It occurs throughout Europe south of

* Because of difficulties in surveying this species all population figures should be treated with caution (Hirons 1990, C.R. Shawyer).

latitude 57°N where it is resident with only some young birds dispersing from their natal areas (Cramp 1985). It is a very difficult species to census and accurate population estimates are difficult to achieve. However, in Britain it is considered to have declined from some 18,000 pairs in 1922 to about 12,000 pairs plus 1,000 non-breeding adults in 1932 (Blaker 1934 cited by Batten *et al.* 1990), to 4,500–9,000 pairs in 1968–72 (Sharrock 1976), to 4,400 pairs and about 1,250 non-breeding individuals in 1982–85 (Shawyer 1987). The number of pairs, however, does not necessarily represent the number that breeds each year because breeding can be significantly affected by the availability of small mammals which undergo considerable short-term population fluctuations.

The European population has declined during the twentieth century and is considered to be 97,000–100,000 pairs (Tucker 1991).

In Ireland, although still widespread, the range of the Barn Owl may be contracting and the population declining. This has been confirmed in the east of Ireland where a 1991 survey indicated a dramatic collapse of the population (B. Madden). However, a comprehensive, intensive survey will be required to establish the true distribution and status of the species.

Threats

The loss of prey-rich foraging areas (e.g. through the intensification of grassland management and general improvements in farm hygiene), the destruction of traditional breeding sites, urbanisation and disturbance are the main threats to Barn Owls (Batten *et al.* 1990). The increased use of toxic pesticides (in particular, certain 'second generation' rodenticides such as brodifacoum, bromadiolone, difenacoum and flocoumafen leading to secondary poisoning (Shawyer 1987, Harrison *et al.* 1990)) is considered as a yet unproven threat in Ireland (C.M. Smal) though several poisoning incidents have been reported recently (B. Madden). Persecution by shooting and trapping, collisions with road traffic, trains and overhead wires, drowning and being trapped in buildings are additional hazards faced by the species (Shawyer 1987). Predation by feral Mink, Stoats, Common Rats, Sparrowhawks and Peregrines are possible but very minor threats (Shawyer 1987) and largely irrelevant in Ireland (C.M. Smal).

Conservation

The recently formed Irish Hawk and Owl Trust is undertaking research on the species and promoting the use of nest boxes on farms to enhance the population (B. Madden). At present this work is concentrated in the east of Ireland so there is an urgent need for a comprehensive intensive survey of the Barn Owl and its habitats throughout the country. This should be coupled with the protection and enhancement or restoration of traditional foraging, nesting and roosting sites and the provision of safe nest boxes in traditional and potential habitats. There is also an urgent need for controls on the use of rodenticides, education about their use and the development of rodenticides which are not toxic to birds.

SHORT-EARED OWL

Asio flammeus

Rare

RSPB/J. Lawton Roberts

The Short-eared Owl is a rare and probably intermittent breeding species and a scarce winter visitor, mainly to east coast counties (Hutchinson 1989). In 1977 a nest was found in long heather in a young conifer plantation and hunting observed in the plantation (Jones 1979). Otherwise there are no details of the breeding habitats used in Ireland where the Short-eared Owl is at the western edge of the Palaearctic part of its range. It has been suggested (Sharrock 1976) that the absence of voles must be an important reason for the lack of regular breeding in Ireland. This hypothesis was reinforced by the report that Bank Voles made up the bulk of the diet of the 1977 breeding pair. However, the fact that the Short-eared Owl has not become established or expanded its range in parallel with the spread of the recently introduced Bank Vole (Smal and Fairley 1984) and that it survives adequately in both Iceland (Glue 1977) and on the Isle of Man, where voles are absent, suggests that factors other than food (e.g. competition with resident species; O'Connor 1986) are limiting its establishment as a breeding species in Ireland.

LEG STATUS IRL	RoI Protected	LEG STATUS EUR	Birds Dir	I
	NI Protected		Bern	II
INTL LEG STATUS			Bonn	–
OCCURRENCE IN IRELAND	[S],W	BEZZEL INDEX, IRELAND		17(B), 12(W)
BREEDING PAIRS	0–3	WINTERING NUMBERS		55+
MAIN FOOD	Small mammals and birds			

History of the Species in Ireland

The Short-eared Owl is primarily a winter visitor in very small numbers, recorded mainly on the coast and occasionally inland. The first report of attempted breeding was for the Mullet, Mayo in 1923 (Kennedy *et al.* 1954) and the first record of confirmed breeding was at Cloosh Valley Forest in Galway in 1959 (Ruttledge 1989). In the same year a pair was seen displaying in Wicklow in July and individuals were recorded during the breeding season in Antrim and Donegal (Hutchinson 1989). Although individuals were seen during the breeding season in subsequent years breeding was not confirmed again until 1977 when single pairs nested in Kerry and Limerick. It is almost certain that two further pairs also nested in Limerick in the same year. No breeding owls were found in 1978 but in 1979 four adult owls were located in Limerick in or near the areas where they had bred in 1977 but it was considered that breeding had not taken place (Jones 1979). Breeding has not taken place in this area in the 1980s either although birds have been seen in the summer and in parties of up to three in the winter (E. Jones). A pair bred in Kerry in 1983 (P. Smiddy cited by Hutchinson 1989) and subsequently (F. King) but no details are available.

Current Distribution and Status

Northern Holarctic and Neotropical with some wintering in the United States, locally in Europe and Africa and in India and south-east Asia. In Britain the Short-eared Owl breeds mainly in Wales, northern England and Scotland. On the continent it is confined as a breeding species to localised populations, mainly in Denmark, Germany, the Netherlands, Belgium and France where there are fewer than 100 pairs (Lecomte and Sylvestre 1991). It is more widespread and numerous in Fenno-Scandia and Iceland. In Britain there are 1,500–2,000 pairs and perhaps more in a good vole year, and in Europe there are 18,300 pairs – the vast majority breeding in Fenno-Scandia.

In Ireland its most recent breeding sites have been in the southern half of the country where a possible maximum of four pairs has bred in any one year. During the 1988–90 period of the New Breeding Atlas survey birds were seen but not noted as breeding in Antrim, Down, Londonderry, Sligo, Roscommon and Cork (Gibbons *et al.* in press).

Threats

None known.

Conservation

Routine recording and the protection of nest sites.

NIGHTJAR

Caprimulgus europaeus **Endangered**

RSPB/S.C. Porter

The Nightjar is now a rare and possibly intermittent breeding species in Ireland. It has been reported nesting in a variety of habitats including uncultivated hillsides with bracken and scattered trees and stone walls for song posts, blanket and raised bogs (both virgin and cut-away) with occasional trees, clearings in and the margins of newly replanted areas in conifer plantations and, occasionally, exposed rocky hillsides and coastal headlands. The majority of recently occupied sites in Ireland has been on elevated terrain but generally below the 300m contour line and well removed from human habitation and disturbance (G. D'Arcy). A recent study in southern Scotland has indicated that virtually all birds occurred on well drained south-east facing slopes and could even live in recently brashed and cleared conifer plantations as well as on more typical heather slopes with scattered trees.

As Ireland is at the north-western edge of the Nightjar's range it is likely that climatic factors have influenced its distribution and status, perhaps indirectly through their effects on its insect prey (Batten *et al.* 1990), though there is apparently no firm evidence for this (Sharrock 1976). It is also likely that its favoured habitats have deteriorated or disappeared as a result of agricultural intensification, including the widespread use of insecticides.

LEG STATUS IRL	RoI Protected	**LEG STATUS EUR**	Birds Dir	I
	NI Protected		Bern	II
INTL LEG STATUS			Bonn	–
OCCURRENCE IN IRELAND	S	**BEZZEL INDEX, IRELAND**		15(B)
BREEDING PAIRS	*c* 30?	**WINTERING NUMBERS**		None
MAIN FOOD	Flying insects, especially moths			

History of the Species in Ireland

Formerly the Nightjar was a regular summer visitor to much of the country and particularly widely distributed in Munster up to the 1950s (Kennedy *et al.* 1954, F. King). In 1952 it was considered to occur at its highest densities west of the River Shannon (Norris 1960). A decline appears to have set in during the 1950s and 1960s and by 1968–72 it was recorded in just one area west of the Shannon and was thinly distributed elsewhere in the country, occurring at a relatively high density only in the Sligo/Leitrim/Fermanagh/Tyrone area (Sharrock 1976). In 1981, in response to a questionnaire to thirty observers who had recorded Nightjars in 1968–72, only one positive response, from Wicklow, was returned (Hutchinson 1989). Two pairs were located on Forth Mountain in Wexford during the years 1984–87 (P.M. Walsh). There was a passage of Nightjars every May on Great Saltee in the 1950s and early 1960s but now passage migrants are very rare – one per three years (O.J. Merne).

Current Distribution and Status

Palaearctic and wintering in the northern Afrotropics (Batten *et al.* 1990). The Nightjar breeds only locally in northern Europe but more widely in the south. In Britain an estimate suggested a population of 3,000–6,000 pairs in 1968–72. In 1981 only 1,784 churring males were recorded and the total number is unlikely to have exceeded 2,000, most of which were in the south of England (Cadbury 1981). The British population continues to decline as do most populations elsewhere in Europe. The total population of north-west Europe is about 22,000 pairs, of which there may be 5,000 pairs in each of France, Germany and Sweden (Batten *et al.* 1990).

In Ireland the current distribution and status of the Nightjar are largely unknown. Undoubtedly, the population, although under-estimated*, is very small and probably in the order of thirty pairs. During the the New Breeding Atlas survey (1988–91) Nightjars were confirmed or probably breeding in Mayo, Tipperary and Kerry. In 1990 it was reported during the breeding season in Mayo (J.K. Partridge), on bog edge and in felled plantations in Tipperary (R.A. Chapman). Small numbers were also recorded, but not reported to be breeding, in Antrim, Londonderry, Donegal, Sligo, Galway (1991) and Waterford (Gibbons *et al.* in press; O'Sullivan and Smiddy 1991). Four churring birds were recorded in the Knockmealdown Mountains in 1991 on plantation edge (C.J. Wilson). There were no published records for Northern Ireland from 1980 to 1985, but a pair was found in Tyrone in 1987 (C. Dawson cited by Hutchinson 1989). In spring 1991 individuals were reported in Armagh, the midlands and the south-east (*IWC News*, Autumn 1991).

---

* Numbers may have been under-estimated because of the bird's habit of churring briefly and late at night.

Threats

Loss of remaining habitat, the increased use of insecticides, human disturbance and climatic change are the main threats to breeding Nightjars in Ireland.

Conservation

No conservation measures have been taken to date. In future, however, the regular reporting of Nightjars and the habitats in which they occur and the creation and maintenance of potential nesting habitat within re-planted conifer plantations would seem to be desirable. It is likely that some records are unreliable because of confusion between the churring of the Nightjar and the reeling song of the Grasshopper Warbler. Therefore, surveys must be conducted with precision and all records thoroughly checked before being accepted.

WOODLARK

Lullula arborea

Extinct

RSPB/S.C. Porter

The Woodlark was a scarce local breeder in Ireland in the last century, becoming extinct about 1900. This was part of an overall contraction in range which is still taking place throughout its Palaearctic range. Climate change seems to have played a part in this as Woodlarks are susceptible to cold winters, but habitat loss – through agricultural intensification and afforestation – is also an important factor (Batten *et al*. 1990). Very few Woodlarks have been recorded in Ireland this century and the species is unlikely to resume breeding in the forseeable future.

LEG STATUS IRL	RoI Protected	LEG STATUS EUR	Birds Dir	I
	NI Protected		Bern	III
INTL LEG STATUS			Bonn	–
OCCURRENCE IN IRELAND	–	BEZZEL INDEX, IRELAND		–
BREEDING PAIRS	–	WINTERING NUMBERS		–

MAIN FOOD Beetles, caterpillars, spiders, other anthropods and seeds

History of the Species in Ireland

Even in the mid 19th century the Woodlark was considered a very local species. Thompson (1849–56) described it as 'not very uncommon' in the Malone area of Belfast and also found it on the shores of Belfast Lough, the

Castlereagh Hills, around Ballynahinch, on the Ards Peninsula and at Rostrevor. It seems to have been present also in Cork and Waterford where, around Cappoquin, Woodlarks were taken as cage birds (Ussher and Warren 1900). These authors also noted its occurrence in Kildare, Offaly, Laois, Wicklow and Dublin between 1850 and 1898. A nest found by Barrington in Wicklow in 1894 was concealed under bracken in a "wild district, full of small dry valleys with some plantations, brows of furze, patches of dead bracken, with cultivation here and there" (Ussher and Warren 1900). By 1900 it was described as one of the rarest and most local of our resident birds and was virtually extinct. A pair bred at Kilbarrow Woods near Ferns, Wexford in 1905 and in 1954 a pair bred near Rosscarbery, Cork. The Woodlark is now a very rare visitor to Ireland with eight non-breeding records this century, the last from Cape Clear in 1966 (Hutchinson 1989).

Current Distribution and Status

West Palaearctic. Breeds mainly between 35°N and 60°N from southern Britain and southern Fenno-Scandia to North Africa, Turkey and the Urals and winters in the southern and western parts of its range. The population has decreased over much of Europe due to habitat destruction, climate changes and human disturbance (Cramp 1988). In Britain the Woodlark breeds in open country with areas of bare ground and very short grass intermingled with areas of long grass, bracken or heather and with scattered trees. The range has contracted since 1850 and by 1988 was confined to south coast counties, Breckland, east Suffolk and south central Wales with numbers estimated at no more than 226 pairs (Batten *et al.* 1990).

Threats

Habitat destruction, combined with the effects of cold winters, is blamed for the loss of Woodlarks from the northern part of its British range. In the absence of specific data from Ireland it can be assumed these factors also played their part in the Irish decline.

Conservation

No measures required.

RING OUZEL

Turdus torquatus — **Rare**

RSPB/H.R. Lowes

The Ring Ouzel is a scarce breeding bird and a passage migrant in spring and autumn. It nests on open uplands, with heather and Bracken, and in areas with rock scree. Its scarcity as a breeding species in Ireland can be attributed to the deterioration in nesting habitat, especially the decline in heather cover and, perhaps, increased disturbance. Other unsubstantiated reasons put forward to explain the decline in Britain include climatic change, competition with Mistle Thrushes and Blackbirds, which have increased considerably in Ireland since the early part of the century (Hutchinson 1989) upland afforestation and agricultural intensification. The contraction of range and decrease in numbers during the first half of the century may have been due to climatic amelioration.

LEG STATUS IRL	RoI Protected	LEG STATUS EUR	Birds Dir	–
	NI Protected		Bern	III
INTL LEG STATUS			Bonn	–
OCCURRENCE IN IRELAND	S,P	BEZZEL INDEX, IRELAND		13(B)
BREEDING PAIRS	50–100	WINTERING NUMBERS		None
MAIN FOOD	Invertebrates and fruits			

History of the Species in Ireland

Although a difficult species to locate and enumerate the Ring Ouzel is said to have bred in most counties at the turn of the century. However, a considerable decrease occurred in the first half of this century (Kennedy *et al.* 1954) and by 1968–72 only small numbers were breeding in Down, Wicklow,

Waterford, Clare, Mayo, Leitrim, Cavan, Donegal and possibly Kerry (Sharrock 1976). Subsequently, breeding was confirmed in Cork in 1977, 1986 and 1987 (Hutchinson 1989), in Kerry continuously from 1982 to 1990 (T.D. Carruthers), in Down, and possibly in Donegal and in Wicklow in 1986, in Down and Wicklow in 1987 and in Wicklow in 1988. There is no suggestion of a break in continuity in Co. Down, where a small number of pairs is seen annually (J.S. Furphy).

Current Distribution and Status

The Ring Ouzel has a fragmented, mainly western Palaearctic range, wintering in southern Spain, north Africa and south-west Asia. In Britain, after a decline to the 1950s, it is now restricted mainly to the uplands of Wales, northern England and Scotland where there are 8,000–16,000 pairs (Marchant *et al.* 1990). Elsewhere in Europe it breeds in Norway, Sweden (5,000 pairs), Finland (20 pairs), Germany (9,000–25,000 pairs), France (1,000–10,000 pairs), northern Spain and Greece (a few tens of pairs). In the absence of population data from Norway the European population must be considered to be in excess of 50,000 pairs.

In Ireland the Ring Ouzel now breeds only in the uplands, mainly in coastal counties. During the 1988–90 period of the New Breeding Atlas survey breeding was confirmed or probable in Antrim, Down, Donegal, Galway, Dublin and Kerry with further reports of birds in Tyrone, Cavan and Offaly (Gibbons *et al.* in press). At least three pairs bred in Wicklow in 1990 (Cooney *et al.* 1991). The size of the breeding population is at present unknown but may be 50–100 pairs.

Threats

Further deterioration of its nesting habitat, primarily as a result of agricultural intensification, is the main threat to the Ring Ouzel in Ireland.

Conservation

No conservation measures have been taken to date. There is, therefore, a need to survey the breeding population, evaluate its nesting habitat and implement conservation management in upland habitats where Ring Ouzels breed or are likely to breed.

WOOD WARBLER

Phylloscopus sibilatrix **Rare**

RSPB/S.C. Porter

The Wood Warbler is a rare breeding species and is a scarce but increasing spring and autumn migrant (Hutchinson 1989). It nests mainly in sessile oak-woods, usually with little secondary growth and sparse ground vegetation (Sharrock 1976). Ireland is on the western edge of its breeding range and its preferred nesting habitat is scarce. However, being a migrant it may also suffer from the competitive advantage of resident species (O'Connor 1986).

LEG STATUS IRL	RoI Protected	LEG STATUS EUR	Birds Dir	–
	NI Protected		Bern	II
INTL LEG STATUS			Bonn	–
OCCURRENCE IN IRELAND	S,P	BEZZEL INDEX, IRELAND		10(B)
BREEDING PAIRS	20+	WINTERING NUMBERS		None
MAIN FOOD Insects				

History of the Species in Ireland

In the nineteenth century the Wood Warbler probably bred regularly in Wicklow, occasionally in Laois and Galway and possibly in Antrim, Fermanagh, Donegal, Sligo, Dublin, Tipperary and Wexford. During the first half of the twentieth century it bred only sporadically, in Wicklow in 1910, Warrenpoint, Down in 1932, Glengarriff, Cork in 1938 and possibly in Wicklow in 1949 (Kennedy *et al.* 1954). In 1968 a pair was proved to breed in Derrybawn in Wicklow and since then one to eighteen singing males have been heard annually in Wicklow and smaller numbers, mainly in the 1980s, in Down, Antrim, Armagh, Fermanagh, Londonderry, Donegal, Sligo (D.C. Cotton), Leitrim, Mayo, Galway, Dublin, Tipperary and Kerry. In 1968 a pair bred in the Erriff Valley, Mayo (Ruttledge 1989).

In Antrim, five woodland sites have been used in three or more years and seven or more in one or two years since 1983. One of these sites, covering 58 acres, has been used annually since 1983 by up to six pairs. Ringing has shown that the birds are not site faithful (N.D. McKee). In the 1984 British Trust for Ornithology Wood Warbler survey singing males or territories were recorded at eleven locations in Antrim, Londonderry and Fermanagh.

Current Distribution and Status

Western Palaearctic and wintering in central Africa. The Wood Warbler breeds in Finland, southern Sweden and southern Norway, Britain and from Denmark south to southern France, Italy and Greece. The population breeding in Britain is probably stable at around 17,000 pairs (Bibby 1989). The species is expanding northwards into Fenno–Scandia but elsewhere in Europe the population seems to be stable. Estimates of the total European population are not presently available.

In Ireland it occurs sporadically in those parts of the country where its preferred oakwood habitat occurs but most commonly and regularly in Wicklow where up to thirteen singing males were recorded in 1986 (O'Sullivan and Smiddy 1987). During the 1988–90 period of the New Breeding Atlas survey it was confirmed or probably breeding in Antrim, Londonderry, Fermanagh, Leitrim, Meath, Dublin and Kerry and birds were also reported in Tyrone, Donegal, Kilkenny and Wicklow (Gibbons *et al.* in press). Four singing males were noted and one pair confirmed breeding in Wicklow in 1990 (Cooney *et al.* 1991) but in 1991 the numbers recorded at traditional sites appeared to have been down on previous years (*IWC News* Autumn 1991). The records suggest that the maximum total in any one year is about twenty pairs. However, as the species is probably overlooked in many areas that total could be higher.

Threats

Further reduction of its nesting habitat would appear to be the main threat to the Wood Warbler in Ireland.

Conservation

Several breeding sites in Northern Ireland and many oakwoods in the Republic are Nature Reserves. However, there is still a need for more intensive searching for nesting Wood Warblers and for the conservation of any remaining unprotected oakwoods.

BEARDED TIT

Panurus biarmicus **Rare**

R.T. Mills

The Bearded Tit is a very rare and intermittent breeding species. Birds may have been resident during the years when breeding was recorded. It nests in reedbeds. Ireland is at the extreme western edge of its range and the cold winters of 1985 and 1986 probably drove the species out of the country. Drainage at Kilcoole, inappropriate reed harvesting at Broad Lough (both in Wicklow) and disturbance may also have contributed to the short duration of its presence in Ireland.

LEG STATUS IRL	RoI Protected	LEG STATUS EUR	Birds Dir	–
	NI Protected		Bern	II
INTL LEG STATUS			Bonn	–
OCCURRENCE IN IRELAND	[R]	BEZZEL INDEX, IRELAND		14(B)
BREEDING PAIRS	Probably none	WINTERING NUMBERS		Very small
MAIN FOOD	Insects and reed seeds			

History of the Species in Ireland

The Bearded Tit was first recorded in Louth in January 1966 and subsequently in Cork in autumn 1972 (Ruttledge 1975). It probably colonised

Ireland during a relatively mild period as a result of an irruption from the Netherlands in the 1970s (Batten *et al.* 1990) but was driven away again by cold winters in the mid-1980s. The first record of breeding was at Kilcoole, Wicklow in 1976 when one pair probably raised two broods. Two females were present again in summer 1977 but it wasn't until 1980 that birds were seen again, though breeding in the intervening period could not be discounted. Up to ten birds were present from January to July 1980. Three or possibly four pairs bred in 1982 and at least eleven pairs were present in 1983, at least three pairs bred in 1984 and two, probably three, in 1985. Breeding may have occurred at Ballycotton, Cork in 1979 and 1980. Subsequently, no birds were recorded until 1990 when one bird was seen at Tacumshin Lake (April and May) and Ring Marsh (mid-June), Wexford, but breeding was not suspected (O.J. Merne; O'Sullivan and Smiddy 1991).

Current Distribution and Status

Palaearctic with a fragmented distribution in Europe and a continuous distribution through southern Asia. In Britain the Bearded Tit was fairly widespread in the early nineteenth century but there was a marked reduction in its range in the first half of this century until it was virtually confined to Norfolk and Suffolk. Subsequently, range expansion has extended its largely coastal distribution north to Yorkshire and south to Dorset with an outlying colony in Lancashire. The current British population is probably about 600 pairs (Batten *et al.* 1990).

In Europe it occurs in Denmark, north Germany and locally in the Netherlands, Belgium, France, Spain, Italy and Greece. The Bearded Tit is very susceptible to cold winters and the European population, for which there are no estimates presently available, probably fluctuates accordingly.

In Ireland the Bearded Tit must now be considered as a casual breeding species with only limited possibilities of returning in the foreseeable future, bearing in mind the small and distant British population.

Threats

Further damage to and inappropriate management of some of its potential breeding sites and cold winters are the main obstacles to the re-establishment of the Bearded Tit as a breeding species in Ireland.

Conservation

Protection of its former breeding haunts could ensure suitable nesting habitat should the Bearded Tit return to Ireland.

TREE SPARROW

Passer montanus — **Indeterminate**

RSPB/H.Blesch

The Tree Sparrow is a scarce resident species which nests mainly in ruined and disused buildings close to the coast. In recent times, however, increasing numbers of birds have been nesting inland in lightly wooded farmland (Chapman 1992).

Ireland is at the western edge of its range. It is suggested (Summers-Smith 1989) that the population increases in Ireland and Britain in the twentieth century resulted from irruptions from continental Europe with the populations subsiding after the irruptions had ceased. If this is true, the major factors influencing the size of the population in Ireland must be operating outside the country. However, there are undoubtedly factors in Ireland and Britain which have had a bearing on the population declines and the following have been suggested as possible candidates:- changing land-use, increased use of agricultural chemicals, destruction of breeding habitats, competition with the House Sparrow and climatic changes (possibly increased rainfall, for example; Summers-Smith 1989).

LEG STATUS IRL	RoI Protected	**LEG STATUS EUR**	Birds Dir	–
	NI Protected		Bern	III
INTL LEG STATUS			Bonn	–
OCCURRENCE IN IRELAND	R	**BEZZEL INDEX, IRELAND**		8(B)
BREEDING PAIRS	< 500?	**WINTERING NUMBERS**		1,000?
MAIN FOOD Seeds and insects				

History of the Species in Ireland

The Tree Sparrow has declined as a breeding species through the twentieth century. It nested in Dublin in the nineteenth century but had gone by the 1940s. Two small colonies disappeared from Kerry by the same time, three Mayo colonies had been deserted by the late 1930s and a Sligo colony had been abandoned by 1948. Colonies also disappeared from Antrim and Londonderry by the late 1940s. Several pairs continued to breed at Dunfanaghy in Donegal up to the early 1950s but those had also gone by 1956. A few pairs bred in Londonderry in 1955, in Down in 1957 and in Antrim in 1958. However, by 1959 and 1960, although there were scattered reports of Tree Sparrows, breeding was not recorded. Breeding was again reported in Londonderry, Donegal and Mayo in 1961 and in Dublin and Down in 1962. By 1965 breeding had been proved in Londonderry, Antrim, Down, Armagh, Donegal, Sligo, Mayo, Galway, Louth, Dublin, Wicklow, Wexford, Waterford and Cork. The colonies were small, usually with less than six pairs, but one in Down had twelve pairs (Ruttledge 1966a).

The population was clearly recovering locally and by 1968–72 breeding was confirmed also in Tyrone, Fermanagh, Leitrim, Roscommon, Kildare, Clare and Kerry and the total population probably amounted to several hundred pairs (Sharrock 1976). However, since that time there appears to have been a reversal in the trend and another contraction of range with breeding birds disappearing, for example, from their former haunts in west Galway and declining in Mayo where only 20 pairs could be found in 1987 (Ruttledge 1989). Small numbers still breed at two sites in Sligo and 10–12 birds have been recorded in the region suggesting perhaps 2–3 pairs with young. A former breeding site near Sligo town has been deserted (D.C. Cotton). However, the Tree Sparrow has increased as a breeding species since its return to Kerry and several new, small colonies have been recorded during the recent New Breeding Atlas survey (F. King).

Current Distribution and Status

Palaearctic, breeding throughout Europe from southern Norway and Sweden to northern and eastern Spain. In Britain the Tree Sparrow breeds mainly in England, east Wales and south and east Scotland. Here the population increased up to the late 1950s and 1960s but has declined strongly since 1976–77. The current population is about 285,000 pairs (Summers-Smith 1989). In continental Europe populations have been fluctuating and no overall trend is apparent. Estimates of the total European population are not presently available.

In Ireland there is still a strong concentration of birds on the east coast from Dublin to Down, in south-east Wexford, and in the Lough Neagh basin, with a scattering of small colonies elsewhere such as north-west Londonderry (D. Allen). The total population may be in the order of three hundred pairs (O.J. Merne). During the 1988–90 period of the New Breeding Atlas survey breeding was confirmed or probable in eighteen counties (Gibbons *et al.* in press; Cooney *et al.* 1991). According to Chapman (1992) the decline of the traditional coastal colonies of the west seems to have been reversed, with more colonies occupied in 1991 than for at least five years.

'Good sized' wintering flocks have been recorded around Lough Foyle but numbers have declined in the past decade (D. Allen). Flocks of 40+ are now recorded in Down in most winters and numbers appear to have increased in both Down and Antrim in recent years (R.A. Brown). Wintering flocks of 60–70 birds were reported on three east coast locations in 1990 and smaller numbers on the coasts of Waterford and Cork (O'Sullivan and Smiddy 1991).

Threats

Changing land-use, increased use of agricultural chemicals, destruction of breeding habitats, competition with the House Sparrow and climatic changes (rainfall in particular) could threaten the long-term viability of the Irish population of Tree Sparrows.

Conservation

The erection of nest boxes on the North Slob, Wexford, has greatly encouraged breeding there, so the erection of nest boxes at traditional sites might have a beneficial effect on the population. In addition, regular recording of Tree Sparrows countrywide and throughout the year should be encouraged.

TWITE

Carduelis flavirostris **Indeterminate**

RSPB/A. Gilpin

The Twite is one of Ireland's least known resident finches which breeds on heather- and Bracken-dominated moorland (Haworth and Thompson 1990), in upland areas and open coastal grassland habitats mainly in the far west (Sharrock 1976). In winter it generally gathers in flocks at the coast on estuaries and saltmarshes (Lack 1986). In Ireland the Twite is at the western edge of a very disjunct range, the heart of which is in central Asia. It was probably never abundant but overgrazing and the loss of heather on coastal uplands have probably contributed to its decline in some areas.

LEG STATUS IRL	RoI Protected	**LEG STATUS EUR**	Birds Dir	–
	NI Protected		Bern	III
INTL LEG STATUS			Bonn	–
OCCURRENCE IN IRELAND	R,[S],W	**BEZZEL INDEX, IRELAND**		17(B),12(W)
BREEDING PAIRS	< 1,000	**WINTERING NUMBERS**		Unknown
MAIN FOOD	Small seeds and insects (summer); saltmarsh plants (winter)			

History of the Species in Ireland

There are indications that the Twite has declined since the beginning of the century, but there is little information on its past status and distribution to support this assertion (Hutchinson 1989). At the end of the nineteenth century it was reported breeding in Waterford, around Lough Neagh and in the mountains of Dublin and Wicklow, all locations where it does not breed today. Generally it breeds on or near the coast in deep heather on steep slopes (H.J. Wilson) and in 1968–72 it was recorded along most of the north and west coastal fringe from Antrim to west Cork with a few inland sites in Londonderry, Mayo and Carlow and possibly also in Sligo and Wexford (Sharrock 1976). It was considered 'tolerably certain that the bird does not breed in Clare' in the 1950s (Kennedy *et al.* 1954). However, it was confirmed breeding there in 1968–72 and during the 1980s (H.J. Wilson) and, in particular, at the Cliffs of Moher (Whilde 1987). Wintering flocks of over 200 birds are reported from time to time, usually on estuaries and coastal wetlands in the north-west, the numbers appearing on the east coast having declined in recent decades (Hutchinson 1989). The largest Northern Ireland flocks have been recorded around Lough Foyle, Londonderry, with over a hundred birds in each flock. Flocks have also been recorded regularly at Lough Beg, Londonderry, in late autumn/early winter for a few days, suggesting that they move from the north-west to favoured wintering areas (R.A. Brown). Flocks winter around Belfast Lough and small numbers have been seen on the coast of Down (D. Allen). As the Twite is considered to be sedentary in Ireland these birds are likely to be the breeding output of the locality, suggesting, perhaps, that the north-west is its breeding stronghold.

Current Distribution and Status

Palaearctic with a strongly disjunct range. The Twite is a bird of the steppe and mountain areas of central and south-west Asia, but with a completely isolated population along the north-west seaboard of Europe, mainly in western Ireland, northern Britain and western Norway (Batten *et al.* 1990).

In Britain the main breeding concentrations are in north and west mainland Scotland, on Orkney, Shetland and the Hebrides, with an isolated population in the southern Penines of England. Population estimates of 25–75 pairs per 10km square in 1968–72 suggested a British population of 19,625 to 58,875 pairs (Davies 1988). No estimates are available for the Norwegian population.

In Ireland the species is now largely restricted to the north and west coastal fringe from Down to west Cork during the breeding season (Gibbons *et al.* in press). In autumn there is some dispersal inland but the numbers involved are very small. On the basis of the density figures suggested for the British population the Irish breeding population would have been in the order of 1,500–4,500 pairs during the 1968–72 period (Sharrock 1976). It seems likely, though, that densities are lower in Ireland and that the population would have been less than indicated. During the 1988–90 New Breeding Atlas survey (Gibbons *et al.* in press) confirmed or probable breeding was recorded in fewer than 50% of the 10km squares in which breeding had been noted in the early 1970s (Sharrock 1976) suggesting that the Twite population has declined substantially and that its population is now considerably less than 1,000 pairs.

Threats

The Twite is threatened by the continued destruction of heather on the coastal uplands and the reduction of food supplies at its wintering sites.

Conservation

The Twite's winter habitat at Sheskinmore, Donegal is a Nature Reserve. Very little is known about the current distribution, population dynamics or general ecology of the Twite in Ireland so a comprehensive survey of the population and its habitats throughout the year is now warranted along with the early conservation of its known breeding areas.

CORN BUNTING

Miliaria calandra **Endangered**

INP/R.H. Thompson

The Corn Bunting is now a rare and endangered resident species, breeding at perhaps only a handful of sites mainly on the west coast of Ireland which is at the western edge of its range. It nests in small fields on the mainland and on offshore islands. Nests are often built in Gorse or Bramble. In Britain the highest densities have been associated with cultivated barley (Thompson and Gribbin 1986).

LEG STATUS IRL	RoI Protected	LEG STATUS EUR	Birds Dir	–
	NI Protected		Bern	III
INTL LEG STATUS			Bonn	–
OCCURRENCE IN IRELAND	R	BEZZEL INDEX, IRELAND		8(B)
BREEDING PAIRS	<100?	WINTERING NUMBERS		<200?
MAIN FOOD	Fruits, seeds and insects			

History of the Species in Ireland

At the turn of the century the Corn Bunting bred in every county except Leitrim and was common in the coastal counties. But by the early 1950s the range had been reduced to islands and cultivated headlands in most coastal counties (Hutchinson 1989). By 1968–72 the only breeding concentrations remaining were in Down, Donegal, Mayo, Galway, Kerry, Cork and Waterford (Sharrock 1976). Numbers continued to decline in the 1970s and the species disappeared from Cork after 1976 and from Kerry (F. King). Corn Buntings have not been recorded breeding in Northern Ireland since the early 1980s (R.A. Brown) but birds were recorded in suitable breeding habitat, near Lisburn, Antrim, in Autumn 1992 (J.K. Partridge). In 1981–84 Corn

Buntings were recorded wintering in one 10km square in Down, one in Donegal, three in Mayo, two in Galway and one in Wexford (Lack 1986). Though the latter survey may have underestimated the population there is no doubt that the species has declined from ubiquity to the edge of extinction during the twentieth century.

Current Distribution and Status

Southern Palaearctic. Resident throughout Europe from southern Sweden to the Mediterranean. In Britain it is now restricted mainly to the lowlands of England and Scotland and has declined by about 42% since the early 1970s (Thompson *et al.* 1992). The population is now likely to be about 25,000–30,000 pairs (Marchant *et al.* 1990). The species is also declining elsewhere in Europe, but no population estimates are presently available, though it is suggested that Europe holds 51–75% of the world population (Tucker 1991).

In Ireland the Corn Bunting is now largely restricted to the coastal areas of Down, Donegal, Mayo, Galway and possibly west Cork with an outlying record in Kildare. However, during the 1988–90 period of the New Breeding Atlas survey breeding was confirmed or probable only in Mayo and Galway (Gibbons *et al.* in press). Several birds were seen at a Mayo haunt in April (A. Walsh) and June 1991. The population is likely to be very much less than the 1,500 pairs estimated for the 1968–72 period (Sharrock 1976) and is now likely to be in the low hundreds or very much less.

There has been one recent (1990) winter record from Down (D. Allen) and another from Wicklow (1992).

Threats

Changing agricultural practices, including the decline in the cultivation of Barley in favour of Wheat and livestock production, field expansion, removal of hedgerows and scrub and earlier harvesting will almost certainly lead to the extinction of the Corn Bunting in Ireland unless immediate action is taken to conserve the nesting and feeding habitats in its few remaining haunts.

Conservation

No conservation measures have yet been taken, so, clearly, there is a very urgent need to estimate the size, structure and distribution of the population, evaluate its habitats and habitat requirements and implement conservation measures wherever there is a breeding population. These measures will include the restoration of traditional arable farming practices, including the cultivation of barley, possibly through the designation of Environmentally Sensitive Areas. The recently-designated ESA at Slyne Head, Galway, includes a Corn Bunting breeding area.

INTERNATIONALLY IMPORTANT SPECIES

Storm Petrel

Hydrobates pelagicus **Internationally Important**

Ireland holds about 50% of the world breeding population (M.L. Tasker).

LEG STATUS IRL	RoI Protected	**LEG STATUS EUR**	Birds Dir	I
	NI Protected		Bern	II
INTL LEG STATUS			Bonn	–
OCCURRENCE IN IRELAND	S, P	**BEZZEL INDEX, IRELAND**		21 (B)
BREEDING PAIRS	50,000–100,000	**WINTERING NUMBERS**		None

MAIN FOOD Marine invertebrates

Whooper Swan

Cygnus cygnus **Internationally Important**

The growing Irish wintering population of over 12,000 birds (Merne and Murphy 1986; Kirby *et al.* 1992) represents 67% of the Icelandic population and 20% of the total European population. Whooper Swans bred successfully for the first time in Ireland in 1992, rearing one young. Previously, rare occurrences of hybridisation with the Mute Swan had been recorded (Hutchinson 1989).

LEG STATUS IRL	RoI Protected	**LEG STATUS EUR**	Birds Dir	I
	NI Protected		Bern	II
INTL LEG STATUS			Bonn	II
OCCURRENCE IN IRELAND	W, [B]	**BEZZEL INDEX, IRELAND**		21 (W)
BREEDING PAIRS	1 (1993)	**WINTERING NUMBERS**		12,000 (1990/91)

MAIN FOOD Freshwater, wetland and pasture plants; some cereals and root crops

Greenland White-fronted Goose

Anser albifrons flavirostris **Internationally Important**

The Irish wintering population now peaks at over 14,000 birds (Norriss and Wilson 1991) representing 50% of the Greenland breeding race.

LEG STATUS IRL	RoI Protected	**LEG STATUS EUR**	Birds Dir	I, II/2, III/3
	NI Protected		Bern	III
INTL LEG STATUS			Bonn	II
OCCURRENCE IN IRELAND	W	**BEZZEL INDEX, IRELAND**		21 (W)
BREEDING PAIRS	None	**WINTERING NUMBERS**		14,000+; increasing

MAIN FOOD Sedge bulbils, grasses, cereals, root crops

Barnacle Goose

Branta leucopsis **Internationally Important**

The Irish wintering population of nearly 9,000 birds (Walsh and Merne 1988; Merne and Walsh in prep) represents nearly 25% of the Greenland breeding population and is slowly increasing.

LEG STATUS IRL	RoI Protected	**LEG STATUS EUR**	Birds Dir	I
	NI Protected		Bern	II
INTL LEG STATUS			Bonn	II
OCCURRENCE IN IRELAND	W	**BEZZEL INDEX, IRELAND**		16 (W)
BREEDING PAIRS	None	**WINTERING NUMBERS**		9,000 (1992/93)

MAIN FOOD Coastal sward, cultivated grasses, some stubble grain, waste potatoes

Light-bellied Brent Goose

Branta bernicla hrota **Internationally Important**

The Irish wintering population which fluctuates between about 16,000 and 24,000 birds (Sheppard in press) represents at least 97% of the Canadian/Greenland population wintering in Europe.

LEG STATUS IRL	RoI Protected	LEG STATUS EUR	Birds Dir	II/2
	NI Protected		Bern	III
INTL LEG STATUS			Bonn	II
OCCURRENCE IN IRELAND	W	BEZZEL INDEX, IRELAND		19 (W)
BREEDING PAIRS	None	WINTERING NUMBERS		18,000 (1992/93)
MAIN FOOD	Seaweeds, eelgrass and coastal grasses			

Peregrine

Falco peregrinus **Internationally Important**

After declining, in common with other European populations in the 1950s and 1960s, the Irish population has increased through the 1970s and 1980s (D.W. Norriss, H.J. Wilson). Preliminary results from a survey in 1991 indicate that the population is still growing (Wilson and Norriss in prep.)

LEG STATUS IRL	RoI Protected	LEG STATUS EUR	Birds Dir	I
	NI Protected		Bern	II
INTL LEG STATUS			Bonn	II
OCCURRENCE IN IRELAND	R	BEZZEL INDEX, IRELAND		21 (B)
BREEDING PAIRS	350+	WINTERING NUMBERS		1,000
MAIN FOOD	Birds			

Chough

Pyrrhocorax pyrrhocorax **Internationally Important**

INP/J. Malins

The breeding population represents nearly 27% of the Western European population (Bignal 1989). Preliminary results from the 1992 Survey indicate a stable or slowly increasing population overall (*IWC News*, Autumn 1992), though the Chough has now virtually disappeared from Northern Ireland and has declined in parts of the west (Berrow *et al.* in prep).

LEG STATUS IRL	RoI Protected	**LEG STATUS EUR**	Birds Dir	I
	NI Protected		Bern	II
INTL LEG STATUS			Bonn	–
OCCURRENCE IN IRELAND	R	**BEZZEL INDEX, IRELAND**		21 (B), 17 (W)
BREEDING PAIRS	656–906 (1992)	**WINTERING NUMBERS**		2,500+

MAIN FOOD Terrestrial and upper littoral invertebrates

AMPHIBIANS

AMPHIBIANS

Common Name	Scientific Name	RDB Category	Page
Species Threatened in Ireland			
Natterjack Toad	*Bufo calamita*	E	138
Internationally Important Species			
Common Frog	*Rana temporaria*	II	142

Key

Ex Extinct
E Endangered
V Vulnerable
R Rare
I Indeterminate
II Internationally Important

NATTERJACK TOAD

Bufo calamita **Endangered**

R.T. Mills

The Natterjack Toad is Ireland's only toad and its rarest amphibian, occurring in just one small area in Kerry. It is adapted primarily to warm and arid environments and is, therefore, restricted over most of its range in Europe to a small number of very characteristic types of habitat (Beebee 1983). In Kerry it lives in coastal sand dunes and breeds in lakes, pools and drains containing water which ranges from fresh to brackish (O'Connor and Jeal 1984). In the early 1990s it bred at 48 sites of which 30 were considered to be tiny, residual sites (M. Gibbons).

In Ireland the species is at the north-western limit of its range and it has never been widespread or numerous. In recent decades its habitat has been fragmented and reduced by human activities.

LEG STATUS IRL	RoI Protected		**LEG STATUS EUR**	Habitats Dir IV
	NI –			Bern II
INTL LEG STATUS				Bonn –

NUMBERS A few hundred adults(?)

MAIN FOOD Aquatic and terrestrial invertebrates

History of the Species in Ireland

Remains of Natterjack Toads were recovered from a megalithic cemetery at Carrowmore, Sligo in the late 1970s. However, it is unclear whether these were contemporary with the pre-historic remains or were the remnants of animals which had burrowed into the soil of the tombs in more recent times (Persson and Persson 1980). Efforts are currently being made to clarify the age and status of these remains (D.C. Cotton).

As the climate during the period of early human occupation was warmer and drier than at present it may be that the species was more widely distributed in Britain and Ireland than it is now (Beebee 1983). However, its mode of arrival is obscure. Beebee (1983) notes that Natterjack Toads have been known in Kerry for nearly two hundred years and that "it seems much more likely that they are truly indigenous' and are part of the 'Lusitanian' biota which is well known in south-west Ireland.

There is no documentary evidence of toads in Ireland prior to 1805 when they were first seen in Callinafersy by Mackay (Mackay 1836, cited by O'Connor and Jeal 1984). Early reports indicated that the species was extremely common around Castlemaine Harbour in the early nineteenth century from where it seems to have undergone a very modest local spread (O'Connor and Jeal 1984) and, latterly, a contraction of range. It occurred at Ballycarbery until two small ponds were drained in 1954 and may also have existed on the Waterville peninsula. It is now confined to coastal sand dunes at Castlegregory and on the peninsulas at the mouth of Castlemaine Harbour.

Current Distribution and Status

The species is restricted to Europe where it occurs in sixteen countries (Corbett 1989) and is the fourteenth most widespread of the continent's 44 amphibian species (Beebee 1983). It is considered to be abundant in Portugal and most of Spain and western France (except Brittany), locally abundant in north-east France and parts of Belgium and locally distributed elsewhere, with its northern limits in southern Sweden and western Russia.

In Britain, where it is classed as "Vulnerable" (Whitten 1990), it was formerly widely but locally distributed in southern and eastern England, on the north-west coast of England and in south-west Scotland. However, the population has declined by 75–80% since the 1940s to about 20,000 adults (Corbett 1989) and the species now occurs at fewer than forty breeding sites (Raw and Pilkington 1988; Whitten 1990), the largest of which are in north-west England and south-west Scotland (Beebee 1983).

In Ireland, Natterjack Toads have never been widespread in historic times, being confined to an area of coastal sand dunes in west Kerry (Figure 7). The population is small and declining as a result of the progressive destruction of its habitat by human activities. It no longer occurs at sites such as Castlemaine, Callinafersy, Cromane and Rosbehy where toads formerly abounded (O'Connor and Jeal 1984).

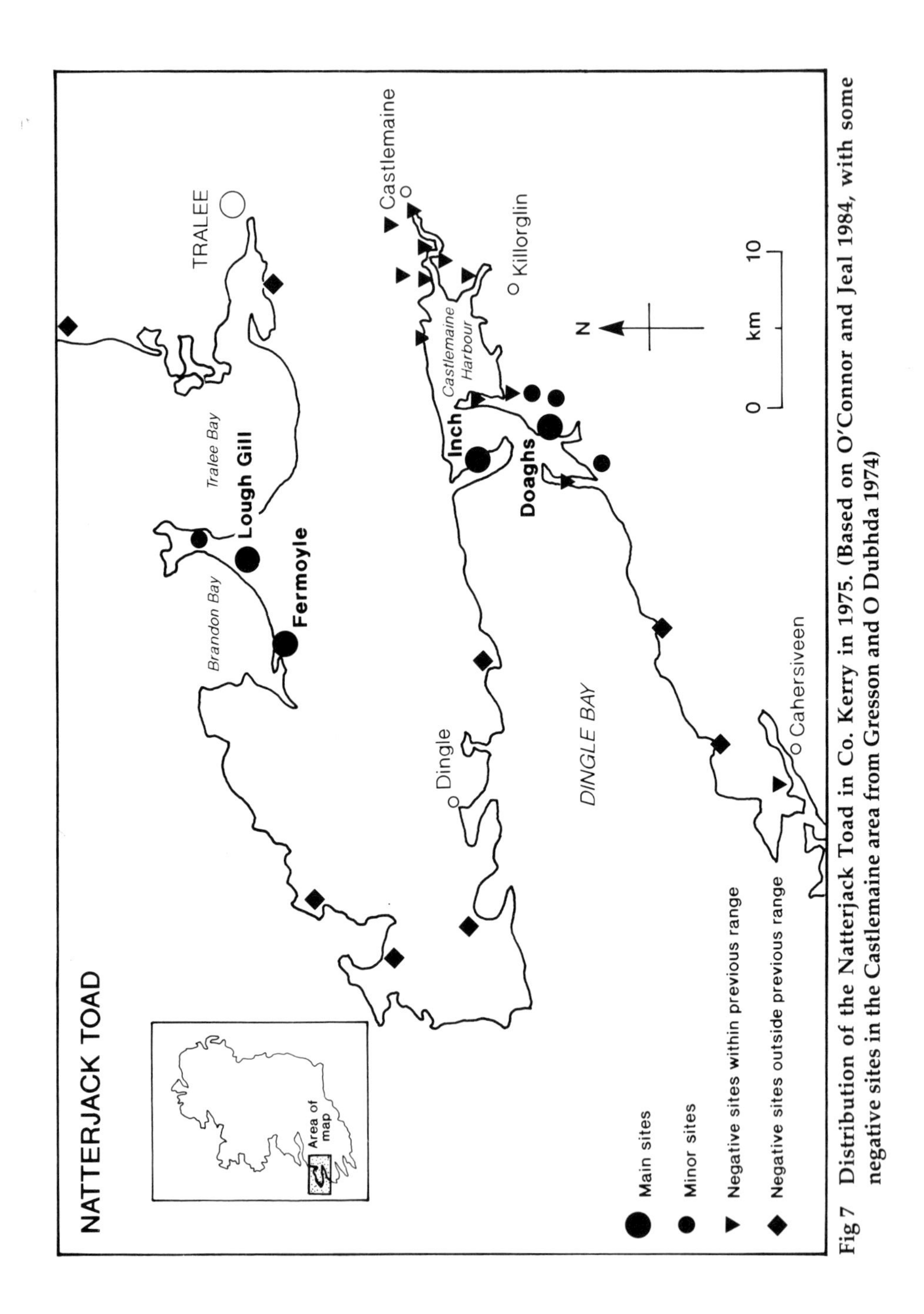

Fig 7 Distribution of the Natterjack Toad in Co. Kerry in 1975. (Based on O'Connor and Jeal 1984, with some negative sites in the Castlemaine area from Gresson and O Dubhda 1974)

In a survey carried out in 1975 O'Connor and Jeal (1984) located 115 adults and in 1979 Buckley (1979) found 291 adults and several toadlets, suggesting the breeding population was then likely to be in the low hundreds. In 1991 all but 7 of the 48 known sites in Kerry were checked for breeding activity and no significant changes from previous years were evident (M. Gibbons).

The species is now considered to be seriously endangered and facing the prospect of extinction by the year 2000 (M.C.D. Speight) unless immediate conservation action is taken.

Threats

Natural threats to the Natterjack Toad include the inundation of the breeding waters by sea water, pond desiccation, the destruction of the dunes by storms, trampling by livestock (Beebee 1983) and predation of adults by fish, birds such as Grey Herons, Wigeon, Black-headed Gulls, and Common Rats. Tadpoles may be taken by Mallard, gulls and carnivorous beetles. In the past the main threat to the species has been the drainage of breeding ponds (M.C.D. Speight). However, the major current threats are from recreational and tourism developments, at least part funded by EC grants. A caravan site threatens Loch Naparka (O'Connor and Jeal 1984), housing is encroaching on Glenveigh and Lough Yganavan, and eutrophication is threatening Lough Gill and Lough Naparka (M. Gibbons). Golf courses, which do not require planning permission, threaten colonies at Lough Gill on the Castlegregory peninsula.

Conservation

The Natterjack Toad is protected under the Wildlife Act (1976) and parts of Lough Yganavan and the whole of Lough Nambrackdarrig are now safeguarded as statutory Nature Reserves. However, the habitats of the remaining viable colonies are not protected by existing legislation.

The case of the nine-hole golf course at Stradbally on the Castlegregory peninsula was put before the Bern Convention in 1991. A delegation visited the area and a subsequent report (Beebee 1991) suggested that habitat management should be undertaken in co-operation with the owners of the Natterjack Toad habitat, particularly with regard to shoreline grazing, water level and water quality regulation in the breeding habitats and the provision of suitable habitat for daytime burrows. The report advised that there should be no further extension of the golf course at Stradbally and that any future golf courses and developments should be directed to sites of low biological interest. It also recommended that a properly-organised survey of Natterjack Toads should be undertaken as soon as possible and a conservation strategy prepared.

The report further recommended that the recently initiated State programme of translocation of Natterjack Toads from the Kerry site to another location in Kerry and to two dune systems (Nature Reserves) in Wexford should be continued.

COMMON FROG

Rana temporaria — **Internationally Important**

The Common Frog is considered to be widespread and common in Ireland but vulnerable in the rest of Europe and the 'Habitats Directive' recommends that its exploitation should be subject to a management plan. The drainage of wetlands, destruction of bogs and water pollution may be adversely affecting the species in some areas of Ireland and a survey of the population may need to be undertaken within about five years.

LEG STATUS IRL	RoI Protected	**LEG STATUS EUR**	Habitats Dir	V
	NI Unprotected*		Bern	III
INTL LEG STATUS			Bonn	–
NUMBERS	Unknown			
MAIN FOOD	Aquatic and terrestrial invertebrates			

* But may not be sold dead or alive at any time.

FISH

FISH

Common Name	Scientific Name	RDB Category	Page
Species Threatened in Ireland			
Sea Lamprey	*Petromyzon marinus*	I	146
River Lamprey	*Lampetra fluviatilis*	I	148
Brook Lamprey	*Lampetra planeri*	I	150
Allis Shad	*Alosa alosa*	E	152
Twaite Shad	*Alosa fallax fallax*	V	154
Killarney Shad	*Alosa fallax killarnensis*	E	156
Arctic Charr	*Salvelinus alpinus*	V	158
Pollan	*Coregonus autumnalis pollan*	E	162
Smelt	*Osmerus eperlanus*	V	166
Internationally Important Species			
Atlantic Salmon	*Salmo salar*	II	168

Key

Ex Extinct
E Endangered
V Vulnerable
R Rare
I Indeterminate
II Internationally Important

SEA LAMPREY

Petromyzon marinus **Indeterminate**

Agence Nature/NHPA

The Sea Lamprey is a native species which inhabits deep offshore waters, shallow inshore waters (Zanadrea 1962 cited by Maitland 1980), estuaries and easily accessible rivers. The adult is parasitic on a wide variety of fish and occasionally on cetaceans such as the Harbour Porpoise. The larva feeds in its burrow on fine particulate matter and micro-organisms (Maitland 1980). It breeds in the unpolluted lower reaches of larger rivers in late May or June when the water temperature reaches at least 15°C, where the gradient of the river bed is shallow, the current slow and where deposition of sand and silt occurs (Maitland 1980).

In Britain it is known to be the rarest of the three lampreys (P.S. Maitland). However, in Ireland lack of information precludes any realistic quantitative evaluation of its status.

LEG STATUS IRL	RoI Unprotected	LEG STATUS EUR	Habitats Dir	II
	NI Unprotected		Bern	–
INTL LEG STATUS			Bonn	–
NUMBERS	Unknown	MIGRATORY STATUS	Mainly anadromous	

MAIN FOOD Larva: micro-organisms, Adult: parasitic on fish

History of the Species in Ireland

The Sea Lamprey is indigenous and considered to be widespread and common in estuaries and easily accessible lakes (D.T.G. Quigley). It spawns in the lower reaches of some of the larger rivers and non-migratory populations have been recorded in Loughs Conn and Corrib and the reservoirs of the River Lee (Went 1978). Returning migratory adults were abundant in the River Fergus at Ennis in the 1960s and in 1984 spawning was recorded in the Mulkear (Mulcair) River at Annacotty, Limerick (M. Kennedy).

Current Distribution and Status

The Sea Lamprey occurs in freshwater from southern Finland, southwards through Denmark to Spain, Italy and southern Greece but is absent from rivers in Iceland, Norway, Sweden and northern Scotland. In the sea it has been recorded from around Iceland and northern Fenno-Scandia southwards into the Mediterranean. It also occurs along the coast and in accessible rivers of eastern North America from Newfoundland to Florida. There are several landlocked populations in North America but not in Europe (Maitland 1980).

In Europe it has declined dramatically in some areas because of pollution and the erection of river barriers (Maitland 1980). In Britain it is considered to be the rarest of the three lampreys and, although not endangered as such, it has lost more populations and is much less common than either of the other Lamprey species (P.S. Maitland).

In Ireland it is considered to be widespread around the coast and in larger estuaries but there are few records with which to assess its current status.

Threats

Increasing pollution could threaten populations in some estuaries.

Conservation

No conservation measures have been taken to date. There is a need for more effective recording of the species wherever it is encountered and for ecological studies of its migratory and non-migratory forms.

RIVER LAMPREY

Lampetra fluviatilis

Indeterminate

Heather Angel

The River Lamprey, or Lampern, is a native species which inhabits shallow inshore waters and accessible rivers. The adult is parasitic, mainly on Herring and Sprat. The larvae feed primarily on micro-organisms including desmids, diatoms and protozoa (Maitland 1980). It breeds in unpolluted freshwater lakes, rivers and streams where the gradient is shallow. In the sea it appears to live in estuarine and inshore waters (Wheeler 1978), possibly staying in areas of low salinity (Bahr 1952 cited by Maitland 1980). There is no specific information available on its habitat in Ireland. Its main breeding locations, however, are in the Lough Neagh catchment area, three rivers in Louth and possibly in the rivers Nore and Bandon (Maitland 1972).

In Ireland the species is at the north-western edge of its range and has probably suffered a diminution in access to spawning areas as a result of the construction of weirs and locks on rivers and an increase in river, estuarine and coastal pollution.

LEG STATUS IRL	RoI Unprotected	**LEG STATUS EUR**	Habitats Dir	II/V
	NI Unprotected		Bern	III
INTL LEG STATUS			Bonn	–
NUMBERS	Unknown	**MIGRATORY STATUS**	Anadromous	

MAIN FOOD Larva: micro-organisms, Adult: parasitic on fish

History of the Species in Ireland

The River Lamprey is indigenous and has probably been present since early post-glacial times. However, little is known about the species as there is no fishery for it in Ireland (Went 1978). It may be fairly widespread but is likely to be rare (D.T.G. Quigley).

Current Distribution and Status

The River Lamprey occurs throughout Europe except in northern Scotland, northern Fenno-Scandia and Iceland. It is migratory and enters rivers from the sea in August-November, and in spring in northern rivers. It has decreased markedly during historical times as a result of the construction of weirs and navigation locks and water pollution. In some rivers where it was once abundant it is now rare (Wheeler 1978). However, it is the most abundant migratory lamprey in west-European rivers (Maitland 1980).

In Ireland it has been recorded in Lough Neagh (Winfield *et al.* 1989) and in a small number of east and south coast rivers (Maitland 1972). Undoubtedly, it is under-recorded and its status is largely unknown.

Threats

The River Lamprey may be threatened locally by increasing pollution and arterial drainage activities.

Conservation

No conservation measures have yet been taken. There is a need for more effective recording of the species whenever it is encountered and ecological studies at its major haunts such as the Lough Neagh catchment area.

BROOK LAMPREY

Lampetra planeri **Indeterminate**

Heather Angel

The Brook Lamprey occurs principally in the Erne catchment area (Maitland 1972) and in "small streams, particularly in the limestone regions of Ireland" (Went 1978; K.F. Whelan). It lives in sandy and gravelly rivers and streams and breeds where the gradient of the river bed is shallow (Maitland 1980). There is no specific information available on its habitat in Ireland. The Brook Lamprey is non-migratory and, therefore, does not occur in the sea. Most of the food taken in by the larvae comes from the superficial sediments, including their microfauna, in the vicinity of their burrows (Moore and Potter 1975). The adults do not feed.

In Ireland the species is at the north-western edge of its range. It may have been introduced and, therefore, it can be speculated that if habitat conditions in Ireland are marginal, it might have been unable to spread. However, if it arrived naturally (see below), other reasons must be found to explain its apparent limited distribution.

LEG STATUS IRL	RoI Unprotected	**LEG STATUS EUR**	Habitats Dir	II
	NI Unprotected		Bern	III
INTL LEG STATUS			Bonn	–
NUMBERS	Unknown	**MIGRATORY STATUS**	Non-migratory	

MAIN FOOD Larva: organic material and microorganisms, Adult: does not feed

History of the Species in Ireland

Although indigenous to Britain it is considered that the Brook Lamprey may have been introduced to Ireland as livebait (Wilson 1983a), though more recent research opens up the possibility of it having arrived naturally (Fryer 1991).

It was very common and widely distributed in small streams as well as rivers. Before arterial drainage commenced it was abundant in all the tributaries of Lough Sheelin. Adults have been obtained from the middle reaches of the River Dodder, Dublin, and young stages from the River Liffey at Altgarvan, Kildare, in recent years (M. Kennedy).

Current Distribution and Status

The Brook Lamprey occurs throughout the Baltic and the North Sea catchment areas in the north, in Britain (except northern Scotland), France, Italy, Sardinia, Albania and probably in Spain and Portugal (Lelek 1980). It is probably the most common lamprey in Europe (Wheeler 1978) although it is now less widespread and numerous than in the past because of 'changes to water courses, particularly corrections, and drastic seasonal variations in water quality, as well as a fall in water quality' (Lelek 1980).

In Ireland most records are concentrated in the north and north-west with one positive record in Cork (Maitland 1972) although Went (1978) states that it is 'fairly widespread, much more than most people would believe'. It is very similar to smaller specimens of the River Lamprey and is considered by some authorities to be merely a non-migratory form of that species (Wheeler 1975). If this is true, and genetic research suggests it to be the case, it becomes possible that the Brook Lampreys arrived naturally in Ireland as River Lampreys which became 'landlocked' (Fryer 1991). Alternatively, others suggest that River and Brook Lampreys are 'paired species' which, though similar in many aspects, remain isolated by various physiological, behavioural and environmental mechanisms (Young 1981; P.S. Maitland).

Threats

Pollution and arterial drainage activities would seem to be the main threats to the Brook Lamprey.

Conservation

No conservation measures have been taken to date. In the absence of any recent information about the Brook Lamprey in Ireland there is a need for more effective recording of the species whenever it is encountered and ecological studies at its major haunts such as the Lough Erne catchment area.

ALLIS SHAD

Alosa alosa **Endangered**

P.S. Maitland

The Allis Shad is a member of the herring family and lives in shallow coastal waters and estuaries and migrates into the lower reaches of larger rivers to spawn during late spring (Went 1953). There is no specific information available on its habitat in Ireland. In continental Europe and in Britain, poor water quality and the construction of weirs and dams are probably the main causes of the demise of the species. These factors may also have affected the Irish population, but there is no evidence available to confirm this. In view of the declines elswhere, and the absence of known spawning populations in Ireland, the species has been classified here as 'Endangered'.

LEG STATUS IRL	RoI Unprotected	LEG STATUS EUR	Habitats Dir	II/V
	NI Unprotected		Bern	III
INTL LEG STATUS			Bonn	–
NUMBERS	Unknown	MIGRATORY STATUS	Anadromous	
MAIN FOOD	Invertebrates, especially plankton			

History of the Species in Ireland

The Allis Shad is presumed to be indigenous and, according to Went (1978), it is found rarely in freshwater and sporadically in estuaries and in the sea off the south-west, north-west and north coasts. There have been no recent records verifying the existence of any spawning populations in Ireland, though the species is probably under-recorded. There are several records from Dingle Bay, Kerry, and two freshwater records, one from Killaloe on the River Shannon in the nineteenth century and another from the Upper Lake of Killarney, Kerry, where a large specimen was found dead on the shore in 1958 (M. Kennedy). Most recent records are from sea captures.

Current Distribution and Status

The Allis Shad occurs in rivers and coastal waters from south Norway southwards to the west coast of Italy. It has become almost extinct in the north of Europe and very rare in the south (Lelek 1980). It is under substantial threat across its whole range and has recently been listed in the U.K. under the Wildlife and Countryside Act (P.S. Maitland). There may now be only one spawning population left in Britain (Maitland and Lyle 1991).

It is not known whether the species is still extant in Ireland. The only specific records since 1960 refer to the presence of the species at one site in the Foyle, at two sites in north Mayo, in the River Corrib in the late 1980s (K.F. Whelan) and at one site in Cork (Maitland 1972).

Threats

Pollution, including thermal pollution, particularly in estuaries (Aprahamian and Aprahamian 1990) would appear to be the main threat to the Allis Shad in Ireland. Barriers and dams are also probably responsible, in part, for the loss of Irish populations (N. O Maoileidigh).

Conservation

The Allis Shad has not yet been subject to any conservation measures. In view of the scarcity of spawning sites in Britain the discovery of spawning sites in Ireland would be of considerable conservation significance (P.S. Maitland) and so it is important that the species be recorded more effectively whenever it is encountered.

TWAITE SHAD

Alosa fallax fallax **Vulnerable**

P.S. Maitland

The Twaite Shad is a member of the herring family and is represented in Ireland by two sub-species, the Twaite Shad, which lives mostly at sea but enters the lower reaches of slow-flowing rivers to spawn, and the non-migratory, lacustrine Killarney Shad (*Alosa fallax killarnensis*). The Twaite Shad is highly sensitive to pollution (Whelan 1989) and the anadromous form may have suffered from river, estuarine and coastal pollution as well as the blocking of rivers by weirs, dams and locks. Like the Allis Shad, substantiative data on the status of the Twaite Shad in Ireland are lacking but in view of both its scarcity and vulnerability it has been classified here as 'Vulnerable'.

LEG STATUS IRL	RoI Unprotected	**LEG STATUS EUR**	Habitats Dir	II/V
	NI Unprotected		Bern	III
INTL LEG STATUS			Bonn	-
NUMBERS	Unknown	**MIGRATORY STATUS**	Anadromous	

MAIN FOOD: Juveniles-plankton and invertebrates; Adults – small marine fish

History of the Species in Ireland

The Twaite Shad is indigenous. The anadromous form has probably been present since early post-glacial times (Wilson 1983a).

Current Distribution and Status

The anadromous form of the Twaite Shad occurs in rivers and coastal waters from north Norway southwards to the west coast of Italy. Lacustrine forms have been recorded in Lake Skuta in Albania and in Italy in lakes Maggiore, Lugano, Como, Iseo, Garda and Lazio (*A.f. lacustris*). The coastal population has decreased drastically in recent years and in the mouths of north European rivers it is considered to be almost extinct (Lelek 1980) and vulnerable elsewhere (Rudge 1984).

In Ireland the anadromous form was originally present along all the east coast but it is now associated with the larger estuaries. The only positive identifications of spawning populations in Irish rivers in recent times (since the 1960s) are for the Suir, Nore and Barrow which flow into Waterford Harbour, and the Cork Blackwater. These have been identified on the spawning beds at spawning time (N. O Maoileidigh). Went and Kennedy (1969) confirmed the presence of shads in these estuaries. Most other records – from the Boyne, Castletown, Nanny, Liffey, Lee, Bandon and Laune (Bracken and Kennedy, 1967; Aprahamian and Aprahamian 1990) – are historical. The Twaite Shad has also been recorded from the Foyle in Londonderry (Aprahamian and Aprahamian 1990). The species has rarely been recorded on the west coast of Ireland (N. O Maoileidigh).

Specimens are caught regularly at sea in pelagic nets and it is highly likely that some of the populations recorded in estuaries are, in fact, feeding shoals rather than spawning populations originating from the rivers (N. O Maoileidgh).

Threats

The main threat to the Twaite Shad is the construction of artificial barriers preventing traditional populations from migrating to spawning beds. This is likely to have been a major factor in the decline of the Irish population. A further important factor is pollution of rivers, estuaries and coastal waters.

Conservation

No efforts have been made to conserve the species. There is a need for more effective recording of the species whenever it is encountered and a comprehensive estuarine survey to locate juvenile stages. Ecological studies, habitat improvement, and control of heavy angling pressure on the River Barrow population (K.F. Whelan) are also required. The location of the spawning areas of the anadromous form will be of considerable conservation significance (P.S. Maitland).

KILLARNEY SHAD

Alosa fallax killarnensis

Endangered

N. O Maoileidigh

The Killarney Shad, or Goureen, is confined to the Killarney Lakes, Co Kerry, occurring mainly in Lough Leane but also in Muckross Lake. This sub-species is non-migratory. The biology of the species and its habitats in Lough Leane have recently been studied by O Maoileidigh (1990). Like the Twaite Shad, this sub-species is highly sensitive to pollution (Whelan 1989) but it is not known how the status of the lacustrine form has changed. The current population is considered small (N. O Maoileidigh).

LEG STATUS IRL	RoI Unprotected	**LEG STATUS EUR**	Habitats Dir	II/V
	NI –		Bern	III
INTL LEG STATUS			Bonn	–
NUMBERS	Unknown	**MIGRATORY STATUS**	Non-migratory	
MAIN FOOD	Mainly plankton; also emerging insects and larger crustaceans			

History of the Species in Ireland

The Killarney Shad is indigenous. Unlike the anadromous form, which has been present since early post-glacial times, it seems the lacustrine sub-species 'did not arrive until well after the glaciation' (Wilson 1983a). This sub-species was first recorded in Lough Leane by C.T. Regan in 1911 (O Maoileidigh *et al.* 1988).

Current Distribution and Status

The Killarney Shad, which is confined to Lough Leane and Muckross Lake, Kerry, differs from the anadromous form in its dwarfed size and larger number of gill rakers carried on the first branchial arch. However, the two forms show a high degree of genetic similarity, suggesting that they are only recently derived from a common population (O Maoileidigh *et al.* 1988). Although these recent findings weaken the case for ascribing sub-specific status to the two populations these authors suggest that, from a practical viewpoint the retention of the sub-species name *killarnensis* deserves serious consideration because it focuses attention on this unique and very important Irish lacustrine population (P.S. Maitland).

Threats

The main threat to the Killarney Shad would appear to be pollution in Lough Leane. Sewage pollution of the Lough has been reduced in recent years and this, presumably, has benefitted the species.

Conservation

No efforts have been made to fully investigate the biology of this species as a basis for conserving it. While more is now known about the Killarney Shad further work is required not only on the species itself but also the lake environment on which it depends. There is a need to locate spawning areas, which may be in shallow bays, and for further studies on population biology and productivity. Continued habitat improvement in Lough Leane is also recommended. Water quality monitoring needs to be carried out as shads are particularly sensitive to organic pollution (O Maoileidigh 1990; K.F. Whelan).

ARCTIC CHARR

Salvelinus alpinus **Vulnerable**

P.S. Maitland

The Arctic Charr, a relative of salmon and trout, represents an arctic-alpine element in the Irish fauna. It occurs mainly in cool, stony, oligotrophic lakes and is confined to freshwater. Spawning occurs in littoral shallows over gravel and stones and, possibly, in tributary streams. In Ireland the species is at the southern edge of its range and it has probably been genetically isolated for about 10,000 years. Pollution, eutrophication, climate change and possibly competition with and predation by native and introduced species have led to a contraction of its range and diminution in numbers in Ireland.

LEG STATUS IRL	RoI Unprotected	**LEG STATUS EUR**	Habitats Dir	–
	NI Unprotected		Bern	–
INTL LEG STATUS			Bonn	–
NUMBERS	Unknown	**MIGRATORY STATUS**	Non-migratory	

MAIN FOOD Invertebrates, especially plankton and fish

History of the Species in Ireland

The Arctic Charr is an indigenous species which was formerly widespread, mainly in the maritime counties (Went 1946) and abundant, but now rare in most places (Went 1971a) and generally restricted to deep lakes in the west

(Figure 8). The Arctic Charr in Ireland is considered to be a landlocked glacial relic of an otherwise anadromous, circumpolar species. Electrophoretic analysis has shown that fish from seven lakes in Ireland and Windermere in England show considerable genetic homogeneity, suggesting that all the populations examined are conspecific and descended from a common ancestor within the past 50,000 years if not in the immediate post-glacial period (Ferguson 1981).

The Arctic Charr of Lough Finn, Donegal and Lough Coomasaharn, Kerry are dwarfed and the latter population is considered to be unique in Ireland and Britain in having 18–19 gill rakers rather than the usual 13–15 on the lower arch. Behnke (1972, cited by Wilson 1983a) has proposed that the Coomasaharn population is a relict of a pre-glacial stock although there is no direct evidence for this as the degree of electrophoretic distinctness of European and Siberian Charrs (from which Behnke suggested the Coomasaharn population was derived) is not known (Ferguson and Fleming 1983, cited by Wilson 1983a). Ferguson (1981) suggests that the two dwarf populations may share a common ancestor with the other Irish populations, with their reduced growth being the result of environmental factors and the increased number of gill rakers in the Coomasaharn Charr developing as an adaptation to its mode of feeding in that lake.

In spite of these pronounced morphological variations Ferguson (1981) considers that all Irish populations should be regarded as forms of *Salvelinus alpinus* and not classified to sub-species level. However, he emphasises that this range of variation and the spectrum of ecological conditions in which these different forms have evolved and presently exist should be borne in mind for conservation purposes.

Current Distribution and Status

Circumpolar. The Arctic Charr is found in landlocked lakes in the mountain districts of Scotland, northern England, Wales (Maitland 1972), northern Russia and the northern regions of North America. It is anadromous in near-Arctic seas (Wheeler 1975).

In Britain the species is locally distributed in over 200 small, isolated and often declining populations (Maitland 1979, 1990; Maitland *et al.* 1991). Elsewhere in Europe the number of populations of Arctic Charr has declined substantially (Maitland and Lyle 1991) and the species is now only locally distributed in small, isolated populations and is considered to be endangered (Lelek 1980).

In Ireland it has been recorded in the lakes shown in Figure 8. These include lakes from which voucher specimens are (or were) available as well as earlier records from the literature (Went 1971a). Many of the records are old and it is suspected that many populations have now become extinct (Went 1978). In Loughs Corrib, Mask and Conn autumn netting in suspected spawning areas in the 1970s revealed large populations of Arctic Charr (M. Kennedy).

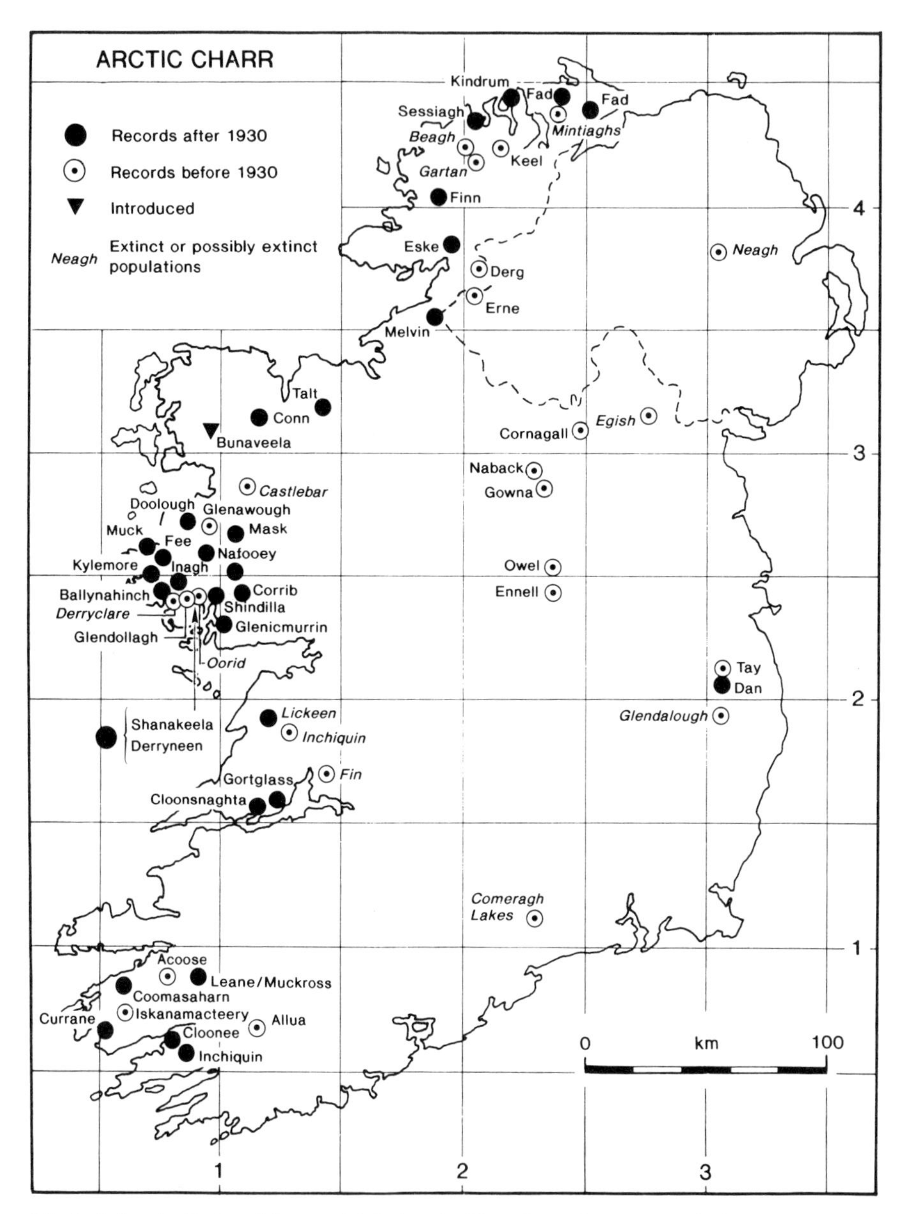

Fig 8 Lakes in Ireland from which Arctic Charr have been recorded (Based on Went 1971a, 1971b, 1978; Quigley and Nolan 1984)

The Irish population is probably now stable and, while populations in some lakes have become extinct, more populations are being discovered (K.F. Whelan). However, there is concern about the population in Lough Conn which is now very small and endangered (W.S.T. Champ).

Threats

The Arctic Charr population is threatened by continued deterioration of water quality (acidification in particular), predation by and competition with native Brown Trout and introduced coarse fish species, intensive industrial fish production and, perhaps, climatic warming. In Scotland there is concern that attempts at cage cultivation of Arctic Charr could threaten the native stocks (Maitland 1990). There are indications from the Bunnaveela system in Mayo and many lakes in Scotland that Arctic Charr grow to exceptionally large sizes (over 3kg) in lakes which are being used to cage-rear juvenile Salmon (Maitland and Campbell 1992). Clearly, the impact of cage-rearing salmonids on Arctic Charr populations needs to be monitored closely.

Conservation

No specific measures have been taken to date. However, water pollution control measures may be helping to stem the decline of the species. It has been suggested that anglers return to the water, unharmed, any specimens taken on rod and line (Whelan 1989). Other conservation measures required include the control of water pollution (primarily from agriculture and forestry), possibly the banning of smolt-rearing and cage-rearing of salmonids in Arctic Charr waters, the control of the transfer of other fish to Arctic Charr waters and the non-acceptance of 'specimen' records.

POLLAN

Coregonus autumnalis pollan **Endangered**

T.J. Pitcher

The Irish Pollan population is the only one in western Europe and is almost unique in being non-migratory, confined to freshwater lakes and so far outside the rest of its world range (Maitland and Lyle 1991). However, for several years after the power station was established on the River Erne between Lower Lough Erne and the estuary Pollan were caught in salmon nets in the estuary. These fish showed faster growth rates in the estuary (Twomey 1956). The Pollan generally lives in large, relatively rich, well oxygenated and clean lakes, although Lough Neagh is relatively shallow and eutrophic. In Lough Neagh it spawns in shallows with a stony and muddy bottom (Dabrowski 1981).

In Ireland the Pollan breeds at the southern limit of its range, isolated from the rest of the world population. Habitat deterioration may have adversely affected all the Irish populations during the twentieth century. In addition, competition with introduced cyprinids may also have been a factor in the population fluctuations, as may have been over-fishing on Lough Neagh on occasions. However, it has also been suggested that population fluctuations such as those recorded on Lough Neagh may have reflected a natural characteristic of whitefish and have been largely attributable to intra-specific competition for planktonic food (Winfield *et al.* 1989).

LEG STATUS IRL	RoI Unprotected	LEG STATUS EUR	Habitats Dir	V
	NI Commercial sp		Bern	III
INTL LEG STATUS			Bonn	-
NUMBERS	Several million	MIGRATORY STATUS	Non-migratory	
MAIN FOOD	Invertebrates, especially plankton			

History of the Species in Ireland

The Pollan is indigenous and probably colonised Ireland from the south-west through the Shannon system when this became ice free (Ferguson *et al.* 1978). It was first described as a separate species by Thompson in 1835 (Ferguson *et al.* 1978). It was originally considered to be conspecific with the Vendace by several authorities including Maitland (1970, 1972) and Wheeler (1975) but recently it has been shown by electrophoretic studies to be identical to the Arctic Cisco, from Alaska, suggesting that the Irish and Alaskan forms are conspecific and have been separated only since the last glaciation (Ferguson *et al.* 1978). Electrophoretic studies have also shown that the Pollan is distinct from the two British species, Vendace and Gwyniad, Powan or Schelly (Ferguson 1974).

The Pollan was once found in large numbers in the Shannon lakes. But between the drainage in the mid-1800s and the 1940s its population declined (Went 1946). There are no recent records of Pollan from Lough Ree (Maitland and Lyle 1991). According to Thompson (1849–56, cited by Went 1946) 'Pollan were probably also to be found in Lough Corrib', but this was contradicted by O'Flaherty (1684) and Went (1946) felt justified in assuming that the Pollan was not indigenous to Lough Corrib.

There have been no records of Pollan from Upper Lough Erne this century and its continued existence in Lower Lough Erne is in some doubt. The Lough Erne population of Pollan once supported a small-scale commercial fishery based on draft- and gill-netting. Pollan captured in bait nets were a favoured bait for Eel lines (Rosell 1993). In 1971 several Pollan were caught accidentally during a gill net survey of Pike stocks. Pollan formed about 5% of the food of the Pike at that time (Rosell 1993).

The Lough Neagh population, which is fished commercially, is moderately well documented (Ferguson 1974, 1975; Ferguson *et al.* 1978; Wilson 1983b, 1984; Wilson and Pitcher 1983, 1984a, 1984b; Dabrowski 1981, 1982a, 1982b,; Dabrowski *et al.* 1984; Winfield *et al.* 1989; Wood 1989).

The Pollan fishery on Lough Neagh rapidly declined in importance relative to the European Eel fishery after 1900 when the former was the more important of the two fisheries and up to 449 tons were sold annually. By 1938 only three tons were being transported from the area and, after an increase during the Second World War, shipments dropped to two tons in 1953. While these figures may not reflect the levels of landings they do indicate the likely trends during the first part of this century. In the early 1970s up to 200 tons were being taken annually and the population in 1976 was estimated at 14 million fish. However, by 1977 the population had dropped to about three million fish and by 1976 commercial fishing had virtually been abandoned (Wood 1982). During the 1980s, however, the Pollan stocks showed an upward trend (Winfield *et al.* 1989).

Current Distribution and Status

There are no other Pollan populations in Europe. There are anadromous populations in western Arctic Canada, northern Alaska and Siberia where they are widespread and common (Wheeler 1975) and showing no evidence of decline (Maitland and Lyle 1991).

In Ireland the Pollan is most abundant in Lough Neagh where, after the decline in the 1970s, the population appears to be increasing (Winfield *et al.* 1989) and may number several millions at present. The species is on the verge of extinction in Lower Lough Erne with only two old fish caught in 1992 (Rosell 1993). Specimens are occasionally taken in eel traps at Killaloe at the southern end of Lough Derg (C. Moriarty) but the current status of the species, both in Lough Derg and in Lough Ree, is unknown.

Threats

The main threats to the Pollan are further habitat deterioration, competition with introduced cyprinids, over-fishing and, perhaps, climatic warming. In Lough Neagh competition with Roach remains a serious threat, but the threat of eutrophication is receding following the apparent success of the introduction of phosphate stripping at the catchment's major sewage treatment works in 1981 (Winfield and Wood 1990).

Conservation

The cessation of fishing on Lough Neagh when the population was low in the 1970s and an amelioration of the habitat in recent years appear to have permitted an increase in the population (though the possibility that natural factors were at least partly, if not totally, responsible for the revival cannot be ruled out (Winfield *et al.* 1989)). However, the commercial fishery, while small, lacks even basic fishery statistics which means that its impact on the stocks cannot be assessed, let alone conservatively managed (Winfield and Wood 1990). Therefore, there is a need to establish the causes of the population fluctuations in Lough Neagh and to implement stringent monitoring and regulation of the fishery if the population is to be managed effectively. In the meantime, habitat protection and amelioration should be continued.

With so few fish remaining on Lower Lough Erne and in the absence of adequate research, conservation action at this site will probably not now be effective.

Little is known about the Pollan in Loughs Derg and Ree and conservation measures are not being applied in these waters. Thus, there is an urgent need to establish the status of these populations and to undertake conservation-orientated ecological research on the two lakes.

It has also been suggested that consideration should be given to establishing one or more new populations in suitable, protected lakes (P.S. Maitland).

SMELT

Osmerus eperlanus **Vulnerable**

P.S. Maitland

The Smelt is a fish which lives in unpolluted estuaries and migrates into large clean rivers to breed just above estuarine limits (Maitland 1972). The Smelt fry feeds on minute planktonic animals, later turning to larger planktonic crustaceans as it grows and finally, as an adult, to larger crustaceans and young fish (Maitland and Lyle 1991). In Ireland it is at the western edge of its range and little is known of its history or ecology in Irish waters. It is, apparently, very susceptible to pollution and in Britain many estuaries have lost populations as a result. The Smelt is believed to be 'Vulnerable' in Ireland (P.S. Maitland) though conclusive evidence to support this is lacking.

LEG STATUS IRL	RoI Unprotected	LEG STATUS EUR	Habitats Dir	–
	NI –		Bern	–
INTL LEG STATUS			Bonn	–
NUMBERS	Unknown	MIGRATORY STATUS	Anadromous	
MAIN FOOD	Invertebrates and fish			

History of the Species in Ireland

It is presumed that the Smelt is indigenous but it has been recorded in only four localities, the estuaries of the Shannon, Fergus and Foyle (Went 1978), from Larne Lough (Moorehead and Service 1992), and from the stomach contents of a Cormorant collected off Little Saltee, Wexford in June 1969 (West *et al.* 1975). The Northern Ireland fish were caught in the past in the intake screens of the Coolkeeragh power station on the shore of Lough Foyle, Londonderry, (Vickers 1974) and at the Ballylumford power station (on the shore of Larne Lough, Antrim) in 1988 and 1989 (Moorehead and Service 1992). The Smelt is said to have been plentiful in the Shannon system and fish ascending to Limerick in March were occasionally caught on worms by trout anglers or in landing nets or even with bare hands by children when the shoals were closely packed (Kennedy 1948).

Current Distribution and Status

The Smelt occurs from the Baltic to the Bay of Biscay and is considered to be moderately common though locally distributed (Wheeler 1975). Estuarine pollution may have reduced populations in some parts of Europe, but there is little recent information to support this suggestion (Lelek 1980). In Britain the species has gone into decline and disappeared from many rivers, mainly as a result of pollution and overfishing – the only exception being the River Thames which it has recolonised as pollution has been reduced (Maitland and Lyle 1991). Several other populations still remain in England (Howes and Kirk 1991) but there is only one left in Wales and three (out of at least eleven) in Scotland (Maitland and Lyle in prep.) of which the River Cree (Hutchinson and Mills 1987) and one other are still exploited (Maitland and Lyle 1991). In all there are said to be 29 river systems with Smelt in the U.K. and Ireland (Hutchinson 1983, cited by Hutchinson and Mills 1987; P. Hutchinson).

Although there are no recent records of Smelt it is likely that it still occurs in the Shannon and it possibly breeds in the lower reaches of rivers from the Shannon, around the south coast to Wexford (D.T.G. Quigley). There were unconfirmed reports of its presence in the Rivers Suir and Nore in 1988 (M. Kennedy). However, a contrary view (C. Moriarty) suggests that, in the absence of records from areas where nets, which should have caught Smelt, have been set and in the absence of any commercial fishery, it is likely that the species is not resident outside the areas mentioned above. Clearly, further research is required to determine the true distribution and status of Smelt in Ireland.

Threats

Estuarine and coastal pollution, reduction in access to its spawning grounds and habitat damage in its spawning and nursery areas will threaten the Smelt in Irish waters.

Conservation

No measures have yet been taken to conserve the Smelt population and it is difficult to prescribe specific measures until more information is collected on the distribution and ecology of the species in Irish waters. Further records from power station and industrial water intake screens would be helpful. In the meantime efforts to ensure that the lower reaches and estuaries of the major rivers on the west and south-west coasts remain free from pollution and structural damage will help to secure the survival of the Irish population of Smelt.

ATLANTIC SALMON

Salmo salar **Internationally Important**

Ireland has a widespread, abundant and self-sustaining population of Atlantic Salmon which, although under pressure from commercial exploitation, is not considered to be threatened at present. Elsewhere in Europe (outside Britain) the species is considered to be endangered, locally threatened or extinct (Lelek 1980).

LEG STATUS IRL	RoI Commercial sp	**LEG STATUS EUR**	Habitats Dir	II/V*
	NI Commercial sp		Bern	III*
INTL LEG STATUS			Bonn	–
NUMBERS	Unknown	**MIGRATORY STATUS**	Anadromous	
MAIN FOOD	Invertebrates and fish			

* Freshwater populations only

5. CONSERVATION OF IRISH RED DATA BOOK VERTEBRATES

HABITATS USED BY RED DATA BOOK SPECIES

The Irish Red Data Book vertebrates utilise a wide range of habitats from woodland to arable land and from man-made structures to the open sea. Habitats used by each species, both for breeding and during winter, are shown in Table 9. The habitat classification follows that used in Britain by the former Nature Conservancy Council for Phase 1 Habitat Survey (NCC 1990).

Woodland and Scrub (1–3)

Ireland has the lowest proportion of broadleaved woodland per unit land area of any country in the EC. However, this is compensated for, to some extent, by the abundance of hedgerows, many with mature trees and shrubs. Woodland edge and hedgerows provide an important feeding habitat for bats and some bats use woodland trees for roosting. Holes in old trees are also used by Barn Owls. Both woodland and hedgerows provide cover for Badgers. Non-native conifers have been widely planted over the past 50 years, many of them on former blanket bog. While afforestation destroys bogland habitats, newly established (pre-thicket) plantations provide nesting habitat for Hen Harrier while Merlin have switched from ground-nesting to nesting in mature trees on plantation edges. Conifer plantation has also encouraged the spread of the Pine Marten and Nightjars can still be found in forestry clearfells. Scrub provides an important feeding habitat for bats, Hen Harrier, Merlin and Nightjar and cover for Grey Partridge and nesting Common Scoter.

Grassland (4–7)

Grass-based agriculture now dominates Irish farming and the amount of arable land is, by comparison, small. This was not always the case; in 1845 there were 8.7 million hectares under grain crops and 7.0 million hectares under root crops (Hutchinson 1989) and, traditionally, Irish agriculture was based on small-scale, unmechanised, mixed farming. It is the disappearance of this agricultural system that has led to the demise of several of the Red Data Book species. Two species that are characteristically associated with low-intensity arable production are Corn Bunting and Grey Partridge. The Corncrake has been the victim of the switch from hay to silage and the loss of prey-rich wetland areas through drainage and herbicide use, although Corncrakes do nest in improved grassland set aside for silage, particularly in Fermanagh. Improved grassland has, however, favoured Greenland

White-fronted Geese, particularly on the Wexford Slobs, and Whooper Swans. Unmanaged rough grassland, particularly along river corridors, provides prey-rich areas for hunting Barn Owls and cover for the Irish Hare. Poor upland grassland, with its populations of Skylark and Meadow Pipit, often forms part of the hunting territory of Merlins and Hen Harriers. Wet, seasonally-flooded, lowland grassland – such as the Shannon Callows and that in the Erne Basin – is an important and threatened habitat for Red Data Book species such as breeding Black-tailed Godwit and Dunlin.

Tall Herb and Fern (8)

This habitat type often provides cover for Red Data Book birds; e.g. Yellow Iris as early-season cover for Corncrakes and Tree Mallow and Nettles for Roseate Terns.

Heath and Bog (9–11)

Ireland's heath and bogland habitats form an internationally-important nature conservation resource and support a number of Red Data Book species. Upland blanket bog and shrub heath provides essential feeding habitats for the upland raptors Merlin and Hen Harrier. Wet blanket bog, often with pools and lakes, is the favoured breeding ground of Golden Plover, Otter and, occasionally, Greenshank. Many of Ireland's Greenland White-fronted Geese formerly wintered on wet blanket bog but this is generally no longer the case. Little is known about Ireland's Twite population, which breeds on blanket bog in the north-west, or the Ring Ouzel whose territories take in blanket bog as well as upland scree.

Fen, Swamp and Freshwater Habitats (12–15)

Reedbeds and tall marginal vegetation – with associated open water – provided a habitat in the past for Bittern and Marsh Harrier, now extinct as breeding species in Ireland. Reedbeds in coastal lagoons still provide breeding habitat for Bearded Tit and Hen Harrier sometimes use reedbeds as a feeding habitat in winter. Marginal vegetation around lowland lakes and rivers provides nesting cover for the Red Data Book waterfowl (Gadwall, Pintail, Garganey, Shoveler and Pochard) while the water bodies themselves provide a variety of food and other needs. Upland lochans on blanket bog are favoured by Red-throated Diver whilst Goosander require fast-flowing salmonid rivers. Many bats feed over and alongside lakes and watercourses, Daubenton's Bat especially. Fish utilise a range of water types from large, clean, slow-flowing rivers (Sea Lamprey, River Lamprey, Allis Shad, Twaite Shad and Smelt) to large lowland lakes (Pollan) to cold, deep lakes in the west and north (Arctic Charr) and clean running water and lakes (Atlantic Salmon and Brook Lamprey). The Killarney Shad is confined to the Killarney Lakes. Otters use all types of water body, even extending to arterially-drained rivers (Chapman and Chapman 1982). Common Frogs favour unpolluted ponds, ditches and bog pools.

Coastal and Marine (16–20, 22)
Ireland's coastal and marine habitats are vitally important to Red Data Book species, supporting many that are of international importance. Otters, for example, utilise indented, weed-covered shorelines such as those of Connemara, while intertidal mud and sand provides winter feeding grounds for Light-bellied Brent Geese, Shoveler, Pintail and waders such as Golden Plover and Dunlin. Many waterfowl, including Common Scoter, use sub-littoral habitats. The latter dive for shellfish on sandy, open coasts. Inshore waters and estuaries are used by the Shads, the Atlantic Salmon and Smelt and by Roseate Tern and Little Tern for feeding. The last two species nest on rocky islands and shingle respectively. The Storm Petrel spends much of the year on the open ocean. Coastal machair on the west and north coasts supports four Red Data Book species – Chough, Dunlin, Natterjack Toad and Red-necked Phalarope. The latter two species require special open-water conditions, hence their very restricted ranges. Sea cliffs in the west and north provide breeding ledges for Peregrine and Chough, but alas, the White-tailed (or Sea) Eagles that they shared them with are long since gone.

Scree and Rock Exposures (21)
Only two species use this habitat: Peregrines breed on ledges in quarries, and Ring Ouzels breed in upland rock scree.

Buildings and Man-made Structures (23)
Decades of rural emigration have left the Irish countryside dotted with old stone buildings – castles, cow-sheds, lime-kilns, churches, cottages and larger farm-houses – many of which are derelict or unused. These buildings, together with structures such as stone-built bridges, provide the main breeding and roosting sites for bats, as well as Tree Sparrow and Chough. Old farm out-buildings were traditionally used by Barn Owls. More modern structures, such as television masts and cranes, are sometimes used as nest sites by Peregrines.

Threats to Red Data Book Species

Many factors combine to influence the status, distribution and population trends of a species. In this Red Data Book adverse factors are treated as threats and are grouped under four main headings:- resource use changes, pollution, killing or disturbance by man and 'natural' threats. A breakdown of threats under each of these headings is presented, for each of the Red Data Book Species in Table 10 and follows closely Batten *et al.* (1990) and Porter *et al.* (1990). Extinct species have been excluded. In some cases our knowledge of the species in Ireland is incomplete which has made the task of assigning threats difficult. Threats may arise quite suddenly and unexpectedly – e.g. the Sand-eel shortage which affected breeding seabirds in Shetland and

TABLE 9: ***Habitats used by Red Data Book vertebrates in Ireland (xx=main habitats; x=secondary habitats; w=wintering habitats).***

	HABITAT																						
	Woodland & Scrub			Grassland				Tall Herb	Heath & Bog			Fen & Swamp		Water		Coastal & Intertidal					Rock	Open Sea	Build -ings
	1	2	3	4	5	6	7	8	9	10	11	12	13	14	15	16	17	18	19	20	21	22	23
THREATENED SPECIES																							
MAMMALS																							
Whiskered Bat	xx			x	x									x	x								xx
Natterer's Bat	xx			x	x									x									xx
Ship Rat																						xx	
BIRDS																							
Red-throated Diver										xx				xx								w	
Black-necked Grebe													xx	xx								w	
Gadwall													xx	xx								w	
Pintail													xx	xx								w	
Garganey													xx	xx									
Shoveler													xx	xx								w	
Pochard													xx	xx								w	
Common Scoter			xx											xx								w	
Goosander															xx							w	
Hen Harrier		xx	xx	xx					xx	xx		w	w										
Merlin		xx		xx					xx	xx	xx												
Grey Partridge			x		x	xx					x												
Corncrake				xx	xx	x	xx	x															
Golden Plover										xx	x					w	w		w				
Dunlin							xx			x	x					w			xx				
Black-tailed Godwit							xx									w	w						
Greenshank										xx						w	w						
Red-necked Phalarope							xx						xx	xx									
Roseate Tern								xx											xx			xx	

Little Tern																		xx		xx	
Barn Owl	xx		x	x	x		x														xx
Short-eared Owl		xx			w						x		w				w				
Nightjar		xx	xx	x				xx	x	x	x										
Ring Ouzel			x	x						x									xx		
Wood Warbler	xx																				
Bearded Tit													xx								
Tree Sparrow	x		x			w														xx	
Twite					w				x	xx							w	w			
Corn Bunting			xx			xx															
AMPHIBIANS																					
Natterjack Toad														xx				xx			
FISH																					
Sea Lamprey														x	xx					xx	
River Lamprey														x	xx					xx	
Brook Lamprey															xx						
Allis Shad															xx					xx	
Twaite Shad															xx					xx	
Killarney Shad														xx							
Arctic Charr														xx	x						
Pollan														xx							
Smelt															xx					xx	
INTERNATIONALLY IMPORTANT SPECIES																					
MAMMALS																					
Hedgehog	xx				xx																
Lesser Horseshoe Bat	xx		x																		xx
Daubenton's Bat	xx		x											xx	xx						xx
Leisler's Bat	xx		x																		xx
Pipistrelle	x		x											x	x						xx
Brown Long-eared Bat	xx	x	x																		xx
Irish Hare				xx	xx		xx			x	x						x				
Pine Marten	x	xx																			
Badger	xx	x	x		x	x	x														
Otter							x			x		x	x	xx	xx	xx		x			

TABLE 9: (Continued)

	HABITAT																						
	Woodland & Scrub			**Grassland**				**Tall Herb**	**Heath & Bog**			**Fen & Swamp**		**Water**		**Coastal & Intertidal**					**Rock**	**Open Sea**	**Build -ings**
	1	**2**	**3**	**4**	**5**	**6**	**7**	**8**	**9**	**10**	**11**	**12**	**13**	**14**	**15**	**16**	**17**	**18**	**19**	**20**	**21**	**22**	**23**
Internationally Important Species (Continued)																							
BIRDS																							
Storm Petrel																			XX	X		XX	
Whooper Swan					X	XX								XX		X							
Greenland W-f. Goose					X	XX				XX	X			X									
Barnacle Goose					XX	X																	
Light-b. Brent Goose					X	X											XX	XX	X			X	
Peregrine										X			W			W		W		XX	XX		X
Chough				X	XX				X								X		XX	XX	X		XX
AMPHIBIANS																							
Common Frog				X	X		XX			X	X	XX	XX	XX									
FISH																							
Atlantic Salmon														XX	XX							XX	

KEY TO HABITATS

1 Broadleaved Woodland
2 Coniferous Woodland
3 Scrub
4 Acid Grassland
5 Neutral Grassland
6 Improved Grassland/Arable
7 Marsh/Marshy Grassland
8 Tall Herb and Fern (e.g. Bracken)
9 Heathland
10 Blanket Bog
11 Raised Bog
12 Fen
13 Swamp, marginal and inundation
14 Standing Water
15 Running Water
16 Intertidal Mud/Sand
17 Intertidal Shingle/Boulders/Rock
18 Saltmarsh
19 Supratidal Sand/Shingle/Boulders/Rock
20 Sea Cliffs and Slopes
21 Rock Exposures and Quarries
22 Sub-littoral Habitats
23 Buildings and man-made structures

Orkney – therefore the threats listed are not necessarily complete and will probably need revising at frequent intervals.

Details of threats to each species are given in the individual Species Accounts. The following paragraphs are, therefore, devoted to a more general consideration of threats.

Resource-use Changes

1. *Agricultural intensification*

Intensive farming methods have had a dramatic and adverse effect on many species – birds and mammals in particular. These include drainage, the conversion of natural or semi-natural habitats into pasture or arable land, reseeding, increasing grazing intensity, burning, hedgerow removal, and the destruction of wetlands, bogs, heaths, coastal machair and sand-dune habitats to create more agricultural land. Also, much greater use of agrochemicals (biocides and fertilisers) and silage, slurry and fertiliser run-off into watercourses.

The species most severely threatened by agricultural intensification include the Grey Partridge (hedgerow removal and loss of small-scale mixed farming), Corncrake (loss of herb-rich meadows and changes in grass harvesting regime), Red-necked Phalarope (drainage and fencing), Corn Bunting (decline in cereal growing, removal of hedgerows), Dunlin (drainage and fencing), Barn Owl (agricultural intensification and 'tidying-up'/replacement of old farm buildings), and Chough (intensification of grassland management on uplands and coastal cliff tops). In contrast, the Whooper Swan and several species of geese have benefited from the intensification of grassland management and intensive cereal and root-crop production.

2. *Agricultural abandonment*

Increasingly, as marginal land becomes less economic to farm it is being abandoned and allowed to return to rank grassland or scrub. Inland, this may have had an adverse effect on the Corncrake and in coastal areas on the Chough.

3. *Afforestation*

In recent decades most conifer afforestation has been undertaken on marginal uplands and blanket bogs. This has had an adverse impact on birds like Merlin, Hen Harrier, and Golden Plover which use blanket bog both for nesting and feeding. Afforestation has also resulted in loss of wintering habitat for the Greenland White-fronted Goose. However, Merlins have, to some extent, adapted to partially afforested moorlands by switching from ground-nesting to tree-nesting and nesting Hen Harriers benefit from the cover provided by young forestry plantation. Nightjars may also benefit from forestry when patchwork clear-felling takes place. Blanket afforestation can cause siltation, shading and acidification of lakes and watercourses affecting fish such as Atlantic Salmon.

4. *Peat extraction*
With the advent of mechanical peat-cutting machines and large-scale exploitation of raised bogs and those blanket bogs which are deep and level enough, peat-cutting is thought to be adversely affecting many moorland and marginal land species through disturbance and loss of habitat. Red-throated Diver, Hen Harrier, Merlin, Golden Plover and Greenland White-fronted Goose are the species most affected by bog destruction.

5. *Felling or destruction of woodland*
Felling of deciduous woodland is no longer a serious threat but felling of hedgerow trees, "tidying up" of woodland areas, and clearance of scrub could affect the food supply of bats and insectivorous birds (e.g. Nightjar). The poor or non-existent management of woods is also a matter of concern. Many woods suffer from overgrazing or rhododendron invasion preventing development of the ground/shrub layers and natural regeneration.

6. *Land reclamation and coastal development*
These activities pose threats mainly to wintering wildfowl and waders, nesting Little Terns, estuarine fish and the Otter, through loss of habitat. The fish most likely to be affected are the Sea and River Lampreys, the Allis and Twaite Shads and the Smelt – the latter in particular because it is thought to inhabit estuaries such as the Shannon which are subject to intensive industrial development.

7. *Fishing intensification*
Any further intensification of fishing effort for Atlantic Salmon at sea could bring this species into the IUCN's 'Commercially Threatened' category. The Pollan fishery on Lough Neagh should be monitored closely to ensure that fishing does not precipitate another decline in the stocks similar to that of the late 1970s.

8. *Other changes in fishery management practices*
The illegal introduction of Roach to many waters in the past two decades has undoubtedly had significant impacts on fish and invertebrate communities, though these remain to be more fully investigated. More care must be taken to prevent the introduction of alien species into Irish waters, particularly those which contain Red Data Book fish species or fish communities of conservation significance (e.g. Lough Melvin).

Fishery management practices should, in future, take into account the requirements of threatened species.

Pollution

9. *Water quality changes*
This includes the acidification of upland lakes – a locally-serious problem in Ireland (e.g. south Connemara) – and the eutrophication of lowland rivers

and lakes through nutrient enrichment. The latter is thought to have affected breeding water birds (especially Common Scoter and possibly Black-necked Grebe) and the aquatic species (amphibians and fish). Many of the fish, in particular species like Arctic Charr, which was once more widespread in Ireland, and Smelt, are susceptible to water-borne pollution whether from agricultural, industrial or domestic sources.

10. *Chemical and pesticide contamination*
The Red Data Book species which are known to be threatened by chemical pollution are the bats (timber treatment in buildings), the Grey Partridge (herbicides and insecticides affecting chick food), and the Barn Owl (secondary poisoning by rodenticides). Although swans and other waterfowl have died of lead poisoning, originating from anglers weights and lead shot, this does not appear to be a serious problem in Ireland (Butler 1990; O' Halloran *et al.* 1991).

11. *Oil pollution*
Although Irish vertebrates have been little affected by oil pollution there is considerable potential for damage, particularly in the vicinity of busy ports. Wintering wildfowl and waders, Otters, breeding seabirds and estuarine fish are most at risk. Amongst Red Data Book species, Roseate Terns and Little Terns nesting in the vicinity of Dublin Port would be vulnerable in the event of an extensive oil spillage.

Killing or Disturbance by Man

12. *Hunting /Fishing*
Gadwall, Pintail, Shoveler, Pochard and Golden Plover may be hunted in both Northern Ireland and in the Republic and Grey Partridge in the Republic only. The wintering influx of large numbers of the first five species negates any threat from hunting. However, in view of the serious decline of Grey Partridge and the small numbers now remaining a total ban on hunting should be considered.

Among the Red Data Book fish species only the Pollan (Lough Neagh) and the Atlantic Salmon are fished commercially on a regular basis and these are subject to modest levels of management and protection. The other species may be caught occasionally on rod and line or as a by-catch of a commercial operation.

13. *Legal (licenced) killing*
This affects quarry species such as the Irish Hare and unprotected species such as the Ship Rat. Licenced killing may also be carried out where a species is considered a 'pest'. However, licences are rarely issued and this is not considered a serious threat to Irish Red Data Book vertebrates at present.

TABLE 10 ***Main threats to the Irish Red Data Book species, excluding extinct species***

	THREAT																				
	Resource-use Changes								Pollution			Killing/Disturbance						'Natural'			
	1	2	3	4	5	6	7	8	9	10	11	12	13	14	15	16	17	18	19	20	21
THREATENED SPECIES																					
MAMMALS																					
Whiskered Bat	●				•					●				•	●		•				
Natterer's Bat	●				•					●				•	●		●				
Ship Rat													●						●		
BIRDS																					
Red-throated Diver	•		●	●					●									•		●	
Black-necked Grebe	●								•											●	●
Gadwall	•								●							●					•
Pintail									●							●					•
Garganey									●							●					•
Shoveler									●			•				●					•
Pochard									●							●					•
Common Scoter								●	●							•			●		●
Goosander			●					•													•
Hen Harrier	●													•							●
Merlin	●		●	•																	
Grey Partridge	●									●		●									●
Corncrake	●	●													●						•
Golden Plover	●		●	●																	•
Dunlin	●		●			●										●					•
Black-tailed Godwit	●																				•
Greenshank	•			•																	•
Red-necked Phalarope	●																	•		●	•
Roseate Tern							•				•								●	●	●
Little Tern						●	•				•					●					●
Barn Owl	●									●				•	●		•	•			
Short-eared Owl																					
Nightjar	●		●													●				●	
Ring Ouzel	●																		•		
Wood Warbler					•																
Bearded Tit						●												•		•	
Tree Sparrow	●																	•			•
Twite			●																		
Corn Bunting	●																	•			
AMPHIBIANS																					
Natterjack Toad						●			●							●		•			•
FISH																					
Sea Lamprey						●			●												
River Lamprey						●			●												
Brook Lamprey									●												
Allis Shad						●			●												
Twaite Shad						●			●												
Killarney Shad									●												
Arctic Charr									●	●		●						•			●

TABLE 10 (Continued)

	THREAT																				
	Resource-use Changes								Pollution			Killing/Disturbance						'Natural			
	1	2	3	4	5	6	7	8	9	10	11	12	13	14	15	16	17	18	19	20	21
FISH (continued)																					
Pollan							●					●						•			●
Smelt						●			●	•											
INTERNATIONALLY IMPORTANT SPECIES																					
MAMMALS																					
Hedgehog																					
Lesser Horseshoe Bat	●									●					●	●	●				
Daubenton's Bat	●									●					●		●				
Leisler's Bat	●									●					●		•				
Pipistrelle	●									●					●		•				
Brown Long-eared Bat	●									●					●		•				
Irish Hare	●																				
Pine Marten										•				•							
Badger														•							
Otter			●						●		•	•		•		●					
BIRDS																					
Storm Petrel																					
Whooper Swan															•						
Greenland W-f. Goose	•		●	●												•					
Barnacle Goose																					
Light-b. Brent Goose																					
Peregrine														•							
Chough	●	●															•				
AMPHIBIANS																					
Common Frog	•								●												
FISH																					
Atlantic Salmon			●	•			●		●			●									•

KEY TO THREATS

Resource-use Changes
1. Agricultural intensification
2. Agricultural abandonment
3. Afforestation
4. Peat extraction
5. Felling or destruction of woodland
6. Land reclamation and coastal development
7. Fishing intensification
8. Other changes in fishery management practices

Pollution
9. Water quality changes
10. Chemical and pesticide contamination
11. Oil pollution

Killing or Disturbance by Man
12. Hunting/Fishing
13. Legal (licensed) killing
14. Illegal persecution
15. Accidental killing
16. Recreational pressure and disturbance
17. Loss of roost sites

'Natural' Threats
18. Climatic change
19. Interspecific competition
20. Natural ecological change
21. Predation, parasitism and disease

GRADES OF THREAT

● Major or principal threat

• Secondary or less important threat

14. *Illegal persecution*

Egg-collecting and taking of bird-of-prey chicks (e.g. for falconry), trapping, shooting and poisoning come under this heading. The first two activities are not known to be threats in Ireland but persistent vigilance will be required to ensure that the nests of threatened birds are not plundered. Hen Harriers have been reported to be subject to persecution because they prey on Red Grouse but with the decline in grouse moors and in keepering this should not be a serious problem in the long term. However, the poisoning of raptors, particularly scavengers of carrion, is a continuing problem because, although the use of strychnine has now been banned, other poisons are still available to farmers for use in crop and stock protection. While the number of suspected poisoning incidents among a formerly scarce species like the Buzzard has increased in recent years – coinciding with the spread of sheep-farming – the spread of this species (Norriss 1991) suggests that illegal persecution is now much less serious than it once was.

Among the mammals, the illegal trapping and shooting of Otters has taken place in parts of the west in recent years and it is also reported that Otters are killed because they are considered a threat to fish farms. The illegal killing of bats is still reported and the problem of Badger-baiting has become widespread in recent years.

15. *Accidental killing*

Road accidents take a regular, but unquantified, toll of Hedgehogs, Irish Hares, Pine Martens, Badgers, Otters and Barn Owls. Otters are accidentally trapped in fish nets and traps. Corncrakes are killed during grass cutting operations and divers and other seabirds are trapped in salmon drift nets (Melville 1973; Whilde 1979). Some Red Data Book species fly into wires; for example Whooper Swans collide with high tension electric cables; Corncrakes and Merlins fly into wire fences.

16. *Recreational pressure and disturbance*

There is little information available on the impact of recreational disturbance on Irish vertebrates though undoubtedly it is widespread and increasing. The Natterjack Toad is threatened by the development of golf courses and other tourism related activities in Kerry.

The increasing use of coastal waters, islands, beaches, sand-dunes and machair poses threats to species such as the Dunlin and Little Tern while intrusive water-sports on loughs and rivers are becoming a hazard to breeding water birds and waders, including several rare ducks, and a disturbance to Otters. The progressive development of water-based activities on the larger lakes and rivers (e.g. Lough Erne, the Shannon) poses a threat to the assemblage of breeding waterbirds for which these sites are important. Hill walking and rock climbing can disturb birds breeding in the uplands and coastal cliff climbing can affect nesting seabirds, Peregrines and Choughs.

Bats such as the Lesser Horseshoe, which is found in caves, are susceptible to disturbance from recreational cavers (C.M. McAney).

17. *Loss of roost sites*
This is a major threat facing the Lesser Horseshoe Bat and other bats which roost in old buildings and other stone structures. Both summer and winter roosts are collapsing through neglect, are being pulled down or completely renovated, resulting in the exclusion of bats. Bridge repair work, often with complete sealing of all crevices, is an important threat to both Daubenton's Bat and the Whiskered Bat (C.M. McAney). The loss of roost sites in old buildings and trees is a factor affecting Barn Owls though specific data for Ireland are lacking.

Natural Threats

18. *Climatic change*
Weather affects all species to some extent, but those living close to the edge of their climatic range are likely to be susceptible to even minor fluctuations. Cold winters during the mid-1980s probably contributed to the disappearance of the Bearded Tit. Cold, wet weather also affects the Barn Owl which is primarily a bird of warmer and drier climates. Poor weather in other parts of their range can reduce the reproductive output of some birds, such as geese, and thereby affect the numbers of those wintering in Ireland.

While short-term weather effects are relatively minor and losses are made good fairly rapidly, large scale climatic changes, such as are predicted as a result of the 'greenhouse effect', are likely to have serious and long-term impacts on some edge-of-range vertebrates. Undoubtedly, the changes accompanying 'global warming' will be more complex than can presently be predicted but one model suggests that the north-western half of Ireland will become windier and wetter while the south-eastern half will become warmer and drier.

The implications of climatic change for Ireland's flora and fauna have been assessed briefly (McWilliams 1991) but clearly, there is much work to be done if they are to be taken into account in any long-term conservation strategy for the Red Data Book vertebrates.

19. *Interspecific competition*
Some species compete with others for breeding sites and food resources. The Roseate Tern, for example, suffers competition for nesting space with large gulls (Batten *et al.* 1990). The Ring Ouzel population may have declined, at least in part, as a result of competition from a growing Blackbird population. The former problem can be controlled, the latter problem would seem to be beyond the scope of management at the present time.

The Common Scoter may have suffered competition for food in Lough

Erne from the introduced Roach (Partridge 1989). With the spread of the latter species in Lough Corrib, coupled with other potentially adverse factors, the future of the Common Scoter on that lake could be in jeopardy. Likewise, the survival of the Rudd – a 'near-threatened species' – is likely to be curtailed by competition from introduced Roach in many waters .

20. *Natural ecological change*

It is often difficult to distinguish natural ecological change from that caused by human activity. However, natural succession in unmanaged vegetation, shifts in the distribution of fish stocks and the natural spread of introduced species such as Cord Grass and American Mink can pose threats to some Red Data Book species. The abandonment of grazing on coastal grasslands can lead to the development of rank vegetation unsuited to the needs of feeding Choughs or breeding waders. Changes in the distribution and population structure of fish such as Sand-eels have seriously affected the breeding success of Arctic Terns and other seabird species in Shetland (Monaghan *et al.* 1989) and possibly Ireland (Whilde 1990).

The spread of Cord Grass in many estuaries has serious implications for wintering wildfowl and waders whose mudflat feeding habitat is reduced as this vigorous alien grass takes over (Nairn 1986).

21. *Predation, parasitism and disease*

Predation is a particularly significant threat to ground nesting birds and these make up a large proportion of the Red Data Book species. It becomes a serious threat when the prey populations occur at low densities or when the habitat has deteriorated for the prey species or improved for the predator (Batten *et al.* 1990). Predation is known to be a serious threat to Little Terns nesting on east coast beaches (O Briain and Farrelly 1990) and to terns and a range of waterbirds nesting elsewhere. Predation by Foxes, Feral Mink, Common Rats, Feral and Domestic Cats, large gulls, Magpies and Hooded Crows needs to be taken into account when considering conservation action.

The inevitable spread of Feral Mink must be monitored closely because, although it is suggested that it does not have a serious long-term impact on common ground nesting waterbirds (Ward *et al.* 1986), it can have a serious effect on breeding duck (Partridge 1992b) and could further endanger species such as the Common Scoter, which nests on islands in the larger western lakes. Likewise, it could pose a threat to breeding terns (Smal 1988; O.J. Merne) and breeding waders which nest on islands and adjacent to lakes and rivers.

The impact of parasites and disease on Irish Red Data Book vertebrates is largely unknown. Parasitic Sea Lice *Lepeophtheirus salmonis* have been implicated in the decline of Sea Trout – a 'near-threatened species' – in the west of Ireland in recent years, though their rôle in the collapse of several fisheries is far from clear at the present time. Infestations of the tapeworm *Ligula intestinalis* caused a temporary reversal in the growth of the Roach population in

Lough Neagh (R.B. Wood), with implications for Red Data Book species occurring in the same waters.

In some areas botulism, caused by the bacterium *Clostridium botulinum*, has seriously reduced populations of Herring Gulls, Lesser Black-backed Gulls and Great Black-backed Gulls and these should be monitored closely in coming years. However, the decline in these competitive and predatory large gulls may benefit breeding terns.

We still know little about the impact of predation, parasitism and disease on vertebrate populations in Ireland, either in terms of their impact on individual animals and populations or their indirect impacts through complex webs of ecological relationships. This dearth of information should make us very wary of introducing new species to Ireland, moving species around within the country, or establishing intensive systems of production for wild species.

Conservation Action

Summary of Conservation Action

The accompanying summary table (Table 11) indicates actions required for 61 Red Data Book species (excluding extinct species) under ten headings. Also included are the fourteen species that just failed to qualify for inclusion under the IUCN criteria but which might be considered near-threatened; these are termed 'Species that Require Monitoring'. The grading of measures as 'High Priority', 'Medium Priority' and 'Lower Priority' takes account of work that has been carried out already or is in progress.

1. *Survey*

Good survey data are available for relatively few Red Data Book species (e.g. Common Scoter, Corncrake, Greenland White-fronted Goose, Barnacle Goose, Light-bellied Brent Goose). A national bat survey is currently in progress in the Republic of Ireland, funded by the National Parks and Wildlife Service. Good distribution data are available for many bird species as a result of Atlas work (Gibbons *et al.* in press) but abundance data are more difficult to come by. Distribution, habitat and abundance data are required for many of the more elusive species, such as the Otter, Barn Owl and Hen Harrier, and the fish, or for those that are thinly distributed over an extensive range e.g. Golden Plover and Curlew. The moorland birds (Red-throated Diver, Hen Harrier, Red Grouse, Golden Plover, Curlew and Twite) in particular need to be surveyed. This work could include a survey of upland screes for Ring Ouzel – a much-neglected species. More survey data are required on birds of marginal farmland such as Barn Owl, Nightjar, Corn Bunting, and on wetland species such as Dunlin and Redshank. Little work has so far been carried out in the Republic on birds of damp grassland (e.g. Redshank, Curlew) in the wider countryside, a habitat which is under threat throughout the EC (Hotker 1991).

The lack of information on population trends of Red Data Book species has been mentioned earlier. The collection of good baseline data will provide a benchmark against which future trends can be compared.

2. *Monitoring*
Monitoring is best described as 'keeping tabs on' a particular species once baseline data are available on distribution, abundance and habitat preferences. All Red Data Book species require monitoring, but priority must be given to the Endangered species. Little is known about the Red Data Book fish so basic ecological survey work will have to be carried out on these before monitoring programmes can be implemented.

Satisfactory data on status and trends are lacking for a substantial number of the 230 species in the regular Irish vertebrate fauna. Efforts are required to improve this situation and to maintain the database on Irish vertebrates which has been compiled alongside this Red Data Book.

3. *Research*
Intensive research may be needed to clarify a particular aspect of the biology of a species. It is often costly and therefore needs to be carefully planned and targeted to ensure that a cost-effective return is achieved. Information on habitat requirements of Red Data Book species is required so that management prescriptions can be prepared for key sites and for use within Environmentally Sensitive Areas (ESA) agreements. Among the various groups the fish stand out as the most poorly known.

4. *Site Conservation*
Examples of specific sites requiring conservation are: bat roosts, rare bird nest sites, bird breeding islands (e.g. Rockabill) and nesting colonies, and individual lakes and river systems for fish and waterbirds. For some species the distinction between site conservation and wider countryside conservation becomes blurred, for example with the Golden Plover where individual stretches of blanket bog (e.g. Cuilcagh, Fermanagh) are important within its north-westerly range. Certain sites are important for a wide range of Red Data Book species and stand out as top priorities amongst sites which need to be conserved (e.g. Lough Corrib, Galway and Lough Erne, Fermanagh).

5. *Wider Countryside Conservation*
Many of Ireland's most threatened species are those that are associated with traditional, low intensity, mixed farming which, combined with the retention of semi-natural habitats, provides a wide range of niches and food resources. The modern-day intensive grassland monoculture has robbed the Irish countryside of many of its micro-habitats and, realistically, it is unlikely that small-scale mixed farming will return in the forseeable future. Probably the best can be hoped for is that ESAs will be applied widely in appropriate areas and that this will enable sufficient habitat to be maintained or

Estuary near Kinsale, Co. Cork.
Large rivers and estuaries on the south coast support rare fish such as Allis Shad, Twaite Shad, Smelt and Lampreys. Populations have decreased greatly in Europe due to pollution and the construction of artificial barriers in river channels. *(Photo: R. T. Mills).*

Sheskinmore Lough, Co. Donegal.
Wet sand-dune machair on the west coast of Ireland is an important habitat for breeding waders, such as Dunlin. Red-necked Phalarope also breed on wet machair at one site in Co. Mayo. *(Photo: R. G. W. Nairn).*

Blanket bog at Owenboy, Co. Mayo.
Wet blanket bog provides breeding habitat for Golden Plover, Dunlin and, occasionally, Greenshank. Afforestation and mechanised peat-cutting are major threats to this habitat in the west of Ireland. *(Photo: P. J. Foss/Irish Peatland Conservation Council).*

Slieveanorra Forest, Co. Antrim.
Good quality heather moorland adjacent to conifer plantation supports breeding Merlin and Hen Harrier, as at this site. *(Photo: J. K. Partridge).*

Lough Corrib, Co. Galway.
The large western lakes (Lough Corrib, Lough Conn and Lough Erne) support a range of threatened species including Common Scoter, Dunlin, Shoveler, Gadwall and Sea Lamprey. These sites are threatened by eutrophication, human disturbance and the spread of Roach and Mink. The Common Scoter, Pollan and Arctic Charr have, consequently, virtually disappeared from Lough Erne and the Arctic Charr is threatened in Lough Conn. *(Photo: The Slide File).*

Reedbed at Strand Lough, Co. Down.
This comparatively small reedbed is an example of the type of habitat occupied by Bearded Tits and once occupied by Marsh Harrier and Bittern, birds that are now extinct in Ireland as breeding species. Extensive reedbeds and swamps have dwindled in size and number throughout Ireland. *(Photo: J. K. Partridge).*

Shannon Callows, Cos. Offaly/Roscommon.
The extensive floodland along the River Shannon, south of Athlone, provides a range of habitats for threatened vertebrates. The hay meadows support a good Corncrake population, Black-tailed Godwits breed on marshy grassland and Shoveler and Pintail breed in marginal vegetation. *(Photo: O. J. Merne).*

Lady's Island Lake, Co. Wexford.
This coastal lagoon supports Europe's second-largest Roseate Tern colony as well as other Red Data Book species such as Garganey and, in the past, Red-necked Phalarope. The lake-level is lowered annually by cutting a channel through the sand bar and this can adversely affect breeding birds. Other problems affecting birds are predation by Common Rats and human disturbance. *(Photo: O. J. Merne).*

re-created for threatened species to maintain a foothold. For example, small-scale cereal cultivation along the western seaboard should be encouraged to help Corn Buntings. Similarly, the control of pollution caused by farm wastes would have a beneficial effect on aquatic species such as the fish. It is also important that efforts are made to survey and protect old, and often derelict, buildings in the countryside as these can provide important roost sites for bats and birds.

Local government also has a part to play in wider countryside conservation and there is evidence that much more could be done to safeguard landscape features such as hedgerows and mature trees, especially alongside roads.

6. *Conservation Legislation*

A summary of national, EC and European conservation legislation applicable to Ireland is provided in Appendix V. The obvious omissions from the list of protected species in both parts of the island are the threatened species of fish, though powers are available under Northern Ireland conservation legislation to protect fish species. Fisheries legislation in Ireland is directed mainly towards the protection of commercially-exploitable fish. However, as the lampreys, the Atlantic Salmon, the shads and the Pollan are now listed in the 'Habitats Directive' as species requiring conservation management, a shift in emphasis towards species conservation will be required. In the Republic, limited protection could be given to these species by the enactment of bye-laws under the Fisheries Consolidation Act, 1959 (and subsequent amendments) prohibiting fishing for them in specified waters or specifying size limits.

7. *Education*

Public education is required concerning all Red Data Book species but there is a particular need for education regarding bats and Badgers which are still viewed with some suspicion and fear. Equally, there is a need to inform decision-makers and local administrators on the plight of Red Data Book species and what can be done to protect them.

8. *Protection from Hunting, Persecution, Disturbance and Accidental Killing*

Many Red Data Book species are vulnerable to these threats. Bats are suffering from the loss of roost sites in old buildings and renovation of existing buildings; birds of prey from illegal shooting, trapping and poisoning; terns from disturbance of breeding colonies; and Corncrakes from accidental killing by grass-cutting machinery. All these threats can be tackled through a combination of better law enforcement, education and further research and monitoring.

Some species are considered vulnerable to legal hunting and the position of the Irish Hare, Gadwall, Shoveler and Golden Plover needs to be reviewed. There is a case to be made for tighter control on hunting Shoveler as the Irish wintering population is quite small at 4,000–8,000 birds. While Ireland plays host to large wintering populations of some Red Data Book waterfowl species it is not clear whether the wintering population also includes the small pool of breeding birds, thus exposing them to hunting pressure. Ringing programmes for these species could help clarify the situation.

More information is required on the effect of commercial fishing on the Pollan.

9. *Predator Control*

Predator control is essential in certain circumstances, e.g. to protect tern colonies from Common Rats, gulls and Foxes. Predation by Foxes is known to be an important factor in the low breeding success of some species (e.g. the Hen Harrier – Bellamy 1989) and predation by corvids could be an important factor in the decline of breeding wader populations (Partridge 1992a). Recent work on Lower Lough Erne suggests that mink predation on semi-colonial breeding waterfowl is controllable. This may be relevant to the protection of the Common Scoter populations on the western lakes but will require additional manpower on the ground. Mink trapping has also been found essential at Lady's Island Lake, Wexford, to protect terns.

10. *Other Measures*

These include sensitive re-pointing of bridges to retain access for bats, the provision of nest boxes for Barn Owls and Tree Sparrows and nest boxes/chick shelters for Roseate Terns, the translocation of species (Natterjack Toad and Pollan) to other sites, the return to the water of rod-caught Red Data Book fish, and the protection of sensitive waters from salmonid cage-culture (Arctic Charr).

Extinct Species

Of the seven extinct species included in the Red Data Book some have a better chance of becoming re-established than others. Steps have been taken already to re-introduce the White-tailed Eagle and a long term programme of introductions and protection is currently underway. Prospects for re-introducing the Golden Eagle are more uncertain and a feasibility study will be required before any such move can be contemplated. The Marsh Harrier and Bittern may re-colonise naturally, though probably not in the near future, particularly in the case of the latter, which is declining in Britain and adjacent parts of Europe. The maintenance and restoration of suitable reedbed habitats, and control of illegal shooting would facilitate this. Both the Woodlark and Capercaillie have little chance of surviving in modern Ireland because of the shortage of suitable habitat and, in the case of the Woodlark, possible climatic change. The Capercaillie could, perhaps, be considered for re-introduction if extensive woodlands were re-created with a significant Scots Pine content.

While it may be desirable to see some of Ireland's extinct species eventually re-introduced, in the short to medium term it may be better to invest scarce resources in protecting the extant fauna, especially in view of the high cost of re-introduction programmes.

Co-ordinated Action for Red Data Book Species

In this chapter an attempt has been made to summarise the main action points arising out of the Species Accounts in this Red Data Book. However, it is recognised that if even one threatened species is to be saved from extinction in Ireland efforts will have to be carefully focussed and the co-operation of a great many people will be required. The preparation of specific Action Plans for particular species is beyond the scope of this book. The appropriate Government Departments, both in Northern Ireland and in the Republic, will now need to study carefully the issues raised in this Red Data Book and to consider further how to tackle the conservation of the species listed.

It is suggested that, as an immediate follow-up to this book, a strategic Action Plan for Red Data Book species be prepared, possibly using the format of Species, Site and Habitat Action Plans developed in Great Britain (Porter *et al.* 1990, Housden *et al.* 1991) or other Action Plans such as those used by the IUCN Species Survival Commission Specialist Groups.

Clearly, however, with some species such as the Corncrake and Grey Partridge, which are on the verge of extinction, there is little time to waste and while Action Plans are being prepared efforts to assist their survival must continue.

Cetaceans

The Steering Committee decided that, due to lack of information, cetaceans (whales, porpoises and dolphins) should not be included in this Red Data Book. Many of the species present in Irish waters are threatened (Evans 1987) and we urgently need better information on their status, numbers, distribution and threats. To this end the Irish Whale and Dolphin Group has recently been set up to gather data on cetacean occurrences. A further encouraging development in the Republic of Ireland is the recent establishment of a cetacean sanctuary covering all Irish waters within the 200 mile European Economic Zone boundary.

Internationally Important Species

This Red Data Book has focussed primarily on Ireland's threatened vertebrates because of the need to highlight the difficulties facing these species. While internationally important species have been included they have not been treated in the text as comprehensively as the threatened species. However, bearing in mind Ireland's international responsibility to conserve these species, there is an equal need to ensure that their conservation needs are addressed. As a follow-up to this study it is suggested that Ireland's unthreatened but internationally important species be similarly investigated and co-ordinated Action Plans prepared for each of them.

TABLE 11: *Summary of conservation action required for Red Data Book species (excluding extinct species) and 'near-threatened' species.*

	ACTION 1	2	3	4	5	6	7	8	9	10
THREATENED SPECIES										
MAMMALS										
Whiskered Bat	⬤	●	●	⬤	•		⬤	⬤		●
Natterer's Bat	⬤	●	●	⬤	•		⬤	⬤		
Ship Rat	•									
BIRDS										
Red-throated Diver	⬤	•	●	⬤						
Black-necked Grebe	⬤	●		●						
Gadwall	●	•		●						
Pintail	●	•		•						
Garganey	●	•		•						
Shoveler	●	•		●				●		
Pochard	●	•		•						
Common Scoter		⬤	●	⬤				•	●	
Goosander	⬤	●		●						
Hen Harrier	⬤	●	•		⬤			●	●	
Merlin	⬤	●	•		⬤			•		
Grey Partridge	⬤	⬤	•		⬤			⬤		
Corncrake		⬤	●	⬤				⬤	•	
Golden Plover	⬤	•	•	⬤	⬤			•		
Dunlin	●	●		●	⬤					
Black-tailed Godwit		●		●				•		
Greenshank		•								
Red-necked Phalarope		●		⬤				•		
Roseate Tern	⬤	⬤	•	⬤				●	⬤	
BIRDS continued										
Little Tern	●	⬤		⬤			•	⬤	⬤	
Barn Owl	⬤	•	●	●	⬤		•	●		•
Short-eared Owl	•			●						
Nightjar	⬤	●	●		⬤					
Ring Ouzel	●	●	●	•						
Wood Warbler	•	●	●	●						
Bearded Tit		•		●						
Tree Sparrow	●	●	•		●					●
Twite	●	•	•							
Corn Bunting	⬤	•	●		⬤					
AMPHIBIANS										
Natterjack Toad	●	⬤	•	⬤						●
FISH										
Sea Lamprey	⬤	●	●	●	●	●	●			
River Lamprey	⬤	●	●	●	●	●	●			
Brook Lamprey	⬤	●	●	●	●	●	●			
Allis Shad	⬤	●	⬤	●	●	●	●			
Twaite Shad	⬤	●	●	●	●	●	●	●		
Killarney Shad	⬤	●	⬤	●		●	●			
Arctic Charr	⬤	●	•	⬤	⬤	●	●			●
Pollan	⬤	●	●	⬤		●	●	⬤		•
Smelt	⬤	●		●		●	●			
INTERNATIONALLY IMPORTANT SPECIES										
MAMMALS										
Hedgehog	•	•								
Lesser Horseshoe Bat	•	●		⬤			⬤	⬤		
Daubenton's Bat	⬤	●		⬤			⬤	⬤		⬤
Leisler's Bat	●	⬤					⬤	●		
Pipistrelle	•	•					⬤	●		
Brown Long-eared Bat	●	●					⬤	●		
Irish Hare	•	•			●			•		
Pine Marten		⬤								
Badger		•								
Otter		●			⬤		•	●		
FISH										
Atlantic Salmon		●			⬤					
BIRDS										
Storm Petrel	●	●								
Whooper Swan		●			•			•		
Greenland W-f. Goose		●	●	⬤	•			●		
Barnacle Goose		●		⬤				•		
Light-b. Brent Goose		●		⬤				•		
Peregrine		•		•				●		
Chough		●	●		⬤					
AMPHIBIANS										
Common Frog	●	●			⬤					

TABLE 11 (Continued)

	ACTION									
	1	2	3	4	5	6	7	8	9	10
SPECIES THAT REQUIRE MONITORING										
BIRDS										
Red Grouse	●	●			●			●		
Curlew	●	●			●			●		
Ringed Plover	●	●								
Redshank	●	●								
Common Sandpiper	●	●								
Razorbill		●								
Puffin		●							•	
Cuckoo	●	●			●					
BIRDS continued										
Kingfisher	●	•								
Dipper	•	●								
Redstart	⬤	●								
FISH										
Brown Trout		●								
Rudd		●								
Nine-spined Stickleback		●								

KEY TO ACTIONS 1–10

1. Survey
2. Monitoring
3. Research
4. Site conservation and management
5. Wider countryside conservation
6. Conservation legislation
7. Education
8. Protection from hunting, persecution, disturbance, accidental killing
9. Predator control
10. Other measures

⬤ High Priority
● Medium Priority
• Lower Priority

APPENDICES

APPENDIX I: SPECIES INCLUDED IN DATABASE OF IRISH VERTEBRATES

NUMBER	COMMON NAME	SCIENTIFIC NAME
MAMMALS		
Extant Species		
1	Hedgehog	*Erinaceus europaeus*
2	Pygmy Shrew	*Sorex minutus*
3	Lesser Horseshoe Bat	*Rhinolophus hipposideros*
4	Whiskered Bat	*Myotis mystacinus*
5	Natterer's Bat	*Myotis nattereri*
6	Daubenton's Bat	*Myotis daubentoni*
7	Leisler's Bat	*Nyctalus leisleri*
8	Pipistrelle	*Pipistrellus pipistrellus*
9	Brown Long-eared Bat	*Plecotus auritus*
10	Rabbit	*Oryctolagus cuniculus*
11	Brown Hare	*Lepus capensis*
12	Irish Hare	*Lepus timidus hibernicus*
13	Red Squirrel	*Sciurus vulgaris*
14	Grey Squirrel	*Sciurus carolinensis*
15	Bank Vole	*Clethrionomys glareolus*
16	Wood Mouse	*Apodemus sylvaticus*
17	House Mouse	*Mus musculus*
18	Ship Rat	*Rattus rattus*
19	Common Rat	*Rattus norvegicus*
20	Fcx	*Vulpes vulpes*
21	Pine Marten	*Martes martes*
22	Irish Stoat	*Mustela erminea hibernica*
23	American Mink	*Mustela vison*
24	Badger	*Meles meles*
25	Otter	*Lutra lutra*
26	Red Deer	*Cervus elaphus*
27	Sika Deer	*Cervus nippon*
28	Fallow Deer	*Dama dama*
29	Feral Goat	*Capra* sp.
30	Common Seal	*Phoca vitulina*
31	Grey Seal	*Halichoerus grypus*
*32	Killer Whale	*Orcinus orca*
*33	False Killer Whale	*Pseudorca crassidens*
*34	Risso's Dolphin	*Grampus griseus*
*35	Long-finned Pilot Whale	*Globiocephala melas*
*36	Common Dolphin	*Delphinus delphis*
*37	Bottle-nosed Dolphin	*Tursiops truncatus*
*38	Atlantic White-sided Dolphin	*Lagenorhynchus acutus*
*39	White-beaked Dolphin	*Lagenorhynchus albirostris*
*40	Striped Dolphin	*Stenella coeruleoalba*
*41	Harbour Porpoise	*Phocaena phocaena*
*42	Northern Bottlenose Whale	*Hyperoodon ampullatus*

* Brief notes only on cetaceans

NUMBER	COMMON NAME	SCIENTIFIC NAME
MAMMALS		
Extant Species (continued)		
*43	True's Beaked Whale	*Mesoplodon mirus*
*44	Sowerby's Beaked Whale	*Mesoplodon bidens*
*45	Cuvier's Beaked Whale	*Ziphius cavirostris*
*46	Blue Whale	*Balaenoptera musculus*
*47	Humpback Whale	*Megaptera novaeangliae*
*48	Northern Right Whale	*Eubalaena glacialis*
Extinct Species		
49	Grey Wolf	*Canis lupus*
BIRDS		
Extant Species		
1	Red-throated Diver	*Gavia stellata*
2	Black-throated Diver	*Gavia arctica*
3	Great Northern Diver	*Gavia immer*
4	Little Grebe	*Tachybaptus ruficollis*
5	Great Crested Grebe	*Podiceps cristatus*
6	Slavonian Grebe	*Podiceps auritus*
7	Black-necked Grebe	*Podiceps nigricollis*
8	Fulmar	*Fulmarus glacialis*
9	Manx Shearwater	*Puffinus puffinus*
10	Storm Petrel	*Hydrobates pelagicus*
11	Leach's Petrel	*Oceanodroma leucorhoa*
12	Gannet	*Morus bassanus*
13	Cormorant	*Phalacrocorax carbo*
14	Shag	*Phalacrocorax aristotelis*
15	Grey Heron	*Ardea cinerea*
16	Mute Swan	*Cygnus olor*
17	Bewick's Swan	*Cygnus columbianus bewickii*
18	Whooper Swan	*Cygnus cygnus*
19	Greenland White-fronted Goose	*Anser albifrons flavirostris*
20	Greylag Goose	*Anser anser*
21	Canada Goose	*Branta canadensis*
22	Barnacle Goose	*Branta leucopsis*
23	Light-bellied Brent Goose	*Branta bernicla hrota*
24	Shelduck	*Tadorna tadorna*
25	Wigeon	*Anas penelope*
26	Gadwall	*Anas strepera*
27	Teal	*Anas crecca*
28	Mallard	*Anas platyrhynchos*
29	Pintail	*Anas acuta*
30	Garganey	*Anas querquedula*
31	Shoveler	*Anas clypeata*
32	Pochard	*Aythya ferina*
33	Tufted Duck	*Aythya fuligula*
34	Scaup	*Aythya marila*
35	Eider	*Somateria mollissima*
36	Long-tailed Duck	*Clangula hyemalis*
37	Common Scoter	*Melanitta nigra*
38	Goldeneye	*Bucephala clangula*
39	Red-breasted Merganser	*Mergus serrator*
40	Goosander	*Mergus merganser*

* Brief notes only on cetaceans

NUMBER	COMMON NAME	SCIENTIFIC NAME
41	Ruddy Duck	*Oxyura jamaicensis*
42	Hen Harrier	*Circus cyaneus*
43	Sparrowhawk	*Accipiter nisus*
44	Buzzard	*Buteo buteo*
45	Kestrel	*Falco tinnunculus*
46	Merlin	*Falco columbarius*
47	Peregrine	*Falco peregrinus*
48	Red Grouse	*Lagopus lagopus*
49	Grey Partridge	*Perdix perdix*
50	Quail	*Coturnix coturnix*
51	Pheasant	*Phasianus colchicus*
52	Water Rail	*Rallus aquaticus*
53	Corncrake	*Crex crex*
54	Moorhen	*Gallinula chloropus*
55	Coot	*Fulica atra*
56	Oystercatcher	*Haematopus ostralegus*
57	Ringed Plover	*Charadrius hiaticula*
58	Golden Plover	*Pluvialis apricaria*
59	Grey Plover	*Pluvialis squatarola*
60	Lapwing	*Vanellus vanellus*
61	Knot	*Calidris canutus*
62	Sanderling	*Calidris alba*
63	Purple Sandpiper	*Calidris maritima*
64	Dunlin	*Calidris alpina*
65	Jack Snipe	*Lymnocryptes minimus*
66	Snipe	*Gallinago gallinago*
67	Woodcock	*Scolopax rusticola*
68	Black-tailed Godwit	*Limosa limosa*
69	Bar-tailed Godwit	*Limosa lapponica*
70	Whimbrel	*Numenius phaeopus*
71	Curlew	*Numenius arquata*
72	Redshank	*Tringa totanus*
73	Greenshank	*Tringa nebularia*
74	Common Sandpiper	*Actitis hypoleucos*
75	Turnstone	*Arenaria interpres*
76	Red-necked Phalarope	*Phalaropus lobatus*
77	Black-headed Gull	*Larus ridibundus*
78	Common Gull	*Larus canus*
79	Lesser Black-backed Gull	*Larus fuscus*
80	Herring Gull	*Larus argentatus*
81	Great Black-backed Gull	*Larus marinus*
82	Kittiwake	*Rissa tridactyla*
83	Sandwich Tern	*Sterna sandvicensis*
84	Roseate Tern	*Sterna dougallii*
85	Common Tern	*Sterna hirundo*
86	Arctic Tern	*Sterna paradisaea*
87	Little Tern	*Sterna albifrons*
88	Guillemot	*Uria aalge*
89	Razorbill	*Alca torda*
90	Black Guillemot	*Cepphus grylle*
91	Puffin	*Fratercula arctica*
92	Rock Dove	*Columba livia*
93	Stock Dove	*Columba oenas*
94	Wood Pigeon	*Columba palumbus*
95	Collared Dove	*Streptopelia decaocto*
96	Turtle Dove	*Streptopelia turtur*

NUMBER	COMMON NAME	SCIENTIFIC NAME
97	Cuckoo	*Cuculus canorus*
98	Barn Owl	*Tyto alba*
99	Long-eared Owl	*Asio otus*
100	Short-eared Owl	*Asio flammeus*
101	Nightjar	*Caprimulgus europaeus*
102	Swift	*Apus apus*
103	Kingfisher	*Alcedo atthis*
104	Skylark	*Alauda arvensis*
105	Sand Martin	*Riparia riparia*
106	Swallow	*Hirundo rustica*
107	House Martin	*Delichon urbica*
108	Tree Pipit	*Anthus trivialis*
109	Meadow Pipit	*Anthus pratensis*
110	Rock Pipit	*Anthus petrosus*
111	Yellow Wagtail	*Motacilla flava*
112	Grey Wagtail	*Motacilla cinerea*
113	Pied Wagtail	*Motacilla alba*
114	Dipper	*Cinclus cinclus*
115	Wren	*Troglodytes troglodytes*
116	Dunnock	*Prunella modularis*
117	Robin	*Erithacus rubecula*
118	Redstart	*Phoenicurus phoenicurus*
119	Whinchat	*Saxicola rubetra*
120	Stonechat	*Saxicola torquata*
121	Wheatear	*Oenanthe oenanthe*
122	Ring Ouzel	*Turdus torquatus*
123	Blackbird	*Turdus merula*
124	Fieldfare	*Turdus pilaris*
125	Song Thrush	*Turdus philomelos*
126	Redwing	*Turdus iliacus*
127	Mistle Thrush	*Turdus viscivorus*
128	Grasshopper Warbler	*Locustella naevia*
129	Sedge Warbler	*Acrocephalus schoenobaenus*
130	Reed Warbler	*Acrocephalus scirpaceus*
131	Whitethroat	*Sylvia communis*
132	Garden Warbler	*Sylvia borin*
133	Blackcap	*Sylvia atricapilla*
134	Wood Warbler	*Phylloscopus sibilatrix*
135	Chiffchaff	*Phylloscopus collybita*
136	Willow Warbler	*Phylloscopus trochilus*
137	Goldcrest	*Regulus regulus*
138	Spotted Flycatcher	*Muscicapa striata*
139	Pied Flycatcher	*Ficedula hypoleuca*
140	Bearded Tit	*Panurus biarmicus*
141	Long-tailed Tit	*Aegithalos caudatus*
142	Coal Tit	*Parus ater*
143	Blue Tit	*Parus caeruleus*
144	Great Tit	*Parus major*
145	Treecreeper	*Certhia familiaris*
146	Jay	*Garrulus glandarius*
147	Magpie	*Pica pica*
148	Chough	*Pyrrhocorax pyrrhocorax*
149	Jackdaw	*Corvus monedula*
150	Rook	*Corvus frugilegus*
151	Hooded Crow	*Corvus corone*
152	Raven	*Corvus corax*

NUMBER	COMMON NAME	SCIENTIFIC NAME
153	Starling	*Sturnus vulgaris*
154	House Sparrow	*Passer domesticus*
155	Tree Sparrow	*Passer montanus*
156	Chaffinch	*Fringilla coelebs*
157	Brambling	*Fringilla montifringilla*
158	Greenfinch	*Carduelis chloris*
159	Goldfinch	*Carduelis carduelis*
160	Siskin	*Carduelis spinus*
161	Linnet	*Carduelis cannabina*
162	Twite	*Carduelis flavirostris*
163	Redpoll	*Carduelis flammea*
164	Common Crossbill	*Loxia curvirostra*
165	Bullfinch	*Pyrrhula pyrrhula*
166	Yellowhammer	*Emberiza citrinella*
167	Reed Bunting	*Emberiza schoeniclus*
168	Corn Bunting	*Miliaria calandra*
Extinct Species		
169	Bittern	*Botaurus stellaris*
170	White-tailed Eagle	*Haliaeetus albicilla*
171	Marsh Harrier	*Circus aeruginosus*
172	Golden Eagle	*Aquila chrysaetos*
173	Capercaillie	*Tetrao urogallus*
174	Woodlark	*Lullula arborea*
REPTILES		
1	Viviparous Lizard	*Lacerta vivipara*
AMPHIBIANS		
1	Smooth Newt	*Triturus vulgaris*
2	Natterjack Toad	*Bufo calamita*
3	Common Frog	*Rana temporaria*
FRESHWATER FISH		
1	Sea Lamprey	*Petromyzon marinus*
2	River Lamprey	*Lampetra fluviatilis*
3	Brook Lamprey	*Lampetra planeri*
4	Allis Shad	*Alosa alosa*
5	Twaite Shad	*Alosa fallax fallax*
6	Killarney Shad	*Alosa fallax killarnensis*
7	Atlantic Salmon	*Salmo salar*
8	Brown/Sea Trout	*Salmo trutta*
9	Rainbow Trout	*Oncorhynchus mykiss*
10	Arctic Charr	*Salvelinus alpinus*
11	Pollan	*Coregonus autumnalis pollan*
12	Smelt	*Osmerus eperlanus*
13	Common Carp	*Cyprinus carpio*
14	Pike	*Esox lucius*
15	Gudgeon	*Gobio gobio*
16	Tench	*Tinca tinca*
17	Bream	*Abramis brama*
18	Minnow	*Phoxinus phoxinus*
19	Rudd	*Scardanius erythrophthamalus*
20	Roach	*Rutilus rutilus*
21	Dace	*Leuciscus leuciscus*
22	Stone Loach	*Noemacheilus barbatulus*
23	European Eel	*Anguilla anguilla*
24	Three-spined Stickleback	*Gasterosteus aculeatus*
25	Nine-spined Stickleback	*Pungitius pungitius*
26	Perch	*Perca fluviatilis*
27	Flounder	*Platichthys flesus*

APPENDIX II: SCIENTIFIC NAMES OF SPECIES MENTIONED IN THE TEXT AND NOT LISTED IN APPENDIX I

MAMMALS

Arctic Fox	*Alopex lagopus*
Brown Bear	*Ursus arctos*
Domestic/Feral Cat	*Felis catus*
Greenland Lemming	*Dicrostonyx torquatus*
Horse	*Equus caballus*
Irish Giant Deer	*Megaloceros giganteus*
Noctule	*Nyctalus noctula*
Norwegian Lemming	*Lemmus lemmus*
Reindeer	*Rangifer tarandus*
Spotted Hyaena	*Crocuta crocuta*
Woolly Mammoth	*Elephas primigenius*

BIRDS

Dotterel	*Charadrius morinellus*
Goshawk	*Accipiter gentilis*
Hawfinch	*Coccothraustes coccothraustes*
Hobby	*Falco subbuteo*
Lesser Whitethroat	*Sylvia curruca*
Montagu's Harrier	*Circus pygargus*
Osprey	*Pandion haliaetus*
Savi's Warbler	*Locustella luscinioides*

FISH

Arctic Cisco	*Coregonus autumnalis*
Gwyniad	*Coregonus lavaretus*
Herring	*Clupea harengus*
Sand Eel	*Ammodytes* spp.
Sprat	*Sprattus sprattus*
Vendace	*Coregonus albula*

PLANTS

Barley	*Hordeum vulgare*
Bilberry	*Vaccinium myrtillus*
Bracken	*Pteridium aquilinum*
Bramble	*Rubus fruticosus*
Common Reed	*Phragmites australis*
Cord Grass	*Spartina* spp.
Cotton Grass	*Eriophorum* spp.
Cranberry	*Vaccinium oxycoccos*
Gorse	*Ulex* spp.
Juniper	*Juniperus communis*
Mat-grass	*Nardus stricta*
Nettle	*Urtica dioica*
Oat	*Avena sativa*
Purple Moor-grass	*Molinia caerulea*
Scots Pine	*Pinus sylvestris*
Sessile Oak	*Quercus petraea*
Tree Mallow	*Lavatera arborea*
Wheat	*Triticum aestivum*
Yellow Iris	*Iris pseudacorus*

APPENDIX III SUMMARY OF KEY DATA FOR RED DATA BOOK VERTEBRATES

		1	2	3	Numbers in Ireland (Birds) 4				Legislation 6					
		RDB Category	Bezzel Index	Status in Ireland	Breeding Pairs		Wintering Numbers		National Legislation 5		EC Birds Directive	EC Habitats Directive	Bern Convention	Bonn Convention
					Est. Min.	Est. Max.	Est. Min.	Est. Max.	RoI	NI				
MAMMALS														
Threatened or Extinct Species														
Whiskered Bat	*Myotis mystacinus*	I	–	–	–	–	–	–	P	P	–	IV	II	–
Natterer's Bat	*Myotis nattereri*	I	–	–	–	–	–	–	P	P		IV	II	–
Ship Rat	*Rattus rattus*	R	–	–	–	–	–	–	U	U	–	–	–	–
Grey Wolf	*Canis lupus*	Ex	–	–	–	–	–	–	–	–	–	II, IV, V	II	–
Internationally Important Species														
Hedgehog	*Erinaceus europaeus*	II	–	–	–	–	–	–	P	U	–	–	III	–
Lesser Horseshoe Bat	*Rhinolophus hipposideros*	II	–	–	–	–	–	–	P	P	–	II,IV	II	–
Daubenton's Bat	*Myotis daubentoni*	II	–	–	–	–	–	–	P	P	–	IV	II	–
Leisler's Bat	*Nyctalus leisleri*	II	–	–	–	–	–	–	P	P	–	IV	II	–
Pipistrelle	*Pipistrellus pipistrellus*	II	–	–	–	–	–	–	P	P	–	IV	III	–
Brown Long-eared Bat	*Plecotus auritus*	II	–	–	–	–	–	–	P	P	–	IV	II	–
Irish Hare	*Lepus timidus hibernicus*	II	–	–	–	–	–	–	Q	Q	–	V	III	–
Pine Marten	*Martes martes*	II	–	–	–	–	–	–	P	P	–	V	III	–
Badger	*Meles meles*	II	–	–	–	–	–	–	P	P	–	–	III	–
Otter	*Lutra lutra*	II	–	–	–	–	–	–	P	P	–	II,IV	II	–
BIRDS														
Threatened or Extinct Species														
Red-throated Diver	*Gavia stellata*	R	18	S,W,P	?	10	200	500	P	P	I	–	II	–

Black-necked Grebe	*Podiceps nigricollis*	R	15	S,W	?	10	?	20	P	P	I	–	II	–
Bittern	*Botaurus stellaris*	Ex	–	W,S	–	–	–	–	P	P	I	–	II	–
Gadwall	*Anas strepera*	R	16	S,W	20	40	400	800	Q	Q	II	–	III	II
Pintail	*Anas acuta*	R	21	S,W	0	1	4000	7500	Q	Q	II,III	–	III	II
Garganey	*Anas querquedula*	R	19	S,P	?	10	0	0	P	P	II	–	III	II
Shoveler	*Anas clypeata*	R	13	R,W,P	100	?	4000	8000	Q	Q	II,III	–	III	II
Pochard	*Aythya ferina*	R	12	S,W	30	?	30000	50000	Q	Q	II,III	–	III	II
Common Scoter	*Melanitta nigra*	E	27	S,W	65	75	3000	5000	P	P	II,III	–	III	II
Goosander	*Mergus merganser*	R	18	S,W	1	2	20	30	P	P	II	–	III	II
White-tailed Eagle	*Haliaeetus albicilla*	Ex*	–	W,S	–	–	–	–	P	P	I	–	II	II
Marsh Harrier	*Circus aeruginosus*	Ex	–	–	–	–	–	–	P	P	I	–	II	II
Hen Harrier	*Circus cyaneus*	E	17	R	50	70	?	150	P	P	I	–	III	II
Golden Eagle	*Aquila chrysaetos*	Ex	–	W,S	–	–	–	–	P	P	I	–	II	II
Merlin	*Falco columbarius*	R	23	R	100	?	300	500	P	P	I	–	II	II
Capercaillie	*Tetrao urogallus*	Ex	–	–	–	–	–	–	P	P	I	–	III	–
Grey Partridge	*Perdix perdix*	E	9	R	?	200	?	1000	Q	P	II,III	–	III	–
Corncrake	*Crex crex*	E	17	S	159	171	0	0	P	P	I	–	II	–
Golden Plover	*Pluvialis apricaria*	V	17	S,W,P,R	300	?	200000	?	Q	Q	I,II,III	–	III	II
Dunlin	*Calidris alpina*	V	19	S,W,P,R	?	300	100000	150000	P	P	–	–	III	II
Black-tailed Godwit	*Limosa limosa*	R	17	S,W,P	2	4	8000	10000	P	P	II	–	III	II
Greenshank	*Tringa nebularia*	R	22	S,W,P	0	1	750	1000	P	P	II	–	III	II
Red-necked Phalarope	*Phalaropus lobatus*	E	22	S,P	0	1	0	0	P	P	I	–	II	II
Roseate Tern	*Sterna dougallii*	E	26	S	503	?	0	0	P	P	I	–	II	–
Little Tern	*Sterna albifrons*	V	15	S	300	?	0	0	P	P	I	–	II	–
Barn Owl	*Tyto alba*	I	10	R	600	900	1200	1400	P	P	I	–	II	–
Short-eared Owl	*Asio flammeus*	R	17	S,W	0	3	55	?	P	P	I	–	II	–
Nightjar	*Caprimulgus europaeus*	E	15	S	30	?	0	0	P	P	I	–	II	–
Woodlark	*Lullula arborea*	Ex	–	–	–	–	–	–	P	P	I	–	III	–
Ring Ouzel	*Turdus torquatus*	R	13	S,P	50	100	0	0	P	P	–	–	III	–
Wood Warbler	*Phylloscopus sibilatrix*	R	10	S,P	20	?	0	0	P	P	–	–	II	–
Bearded Tit	*Panurus biarmicus*	R	14	R	?	?	?	?	P	P	–	–	II	–

APPENDIX III ***(Continued)***

		1 RDB Category	2 Bezzel Index	3 Status in Ireland	4 Numbers in Ireland (Birds): Breeding Pairs Est. Min.	Breeding Pairs Est. Max.	Wintering Numbers Est. Min.	Wintering Numbers Est. Max.	6 Legislation: National Legislation[5] RoI	National Legislation[5] NI	EC Birds Directive	EC Habitats Directive	Bern Convention	Bonn Convention
Tree Sparrow	*Passer montanus*	I	8	R	?	500	1000	?	P	P	–	–	III	–
Twite	*Carduelis flavirostris*	I	17	R,S,W	?	1000	?	?	P	P	–	–	III	–
Corn Bunting	*Miliaria calandra*	E	8	R	?	100	?	200	P	P	–	–	III	–
Internationally Important Species														
Storm Petrel	*Hydrobates pelagicus*	II	21	S,P	50000	100000	0	0	P	P	I	–	II	–
Whooper Swan	*Cygnus cygnus*	II	–	W,B	1	3	12000	?	P	P	I	–	II	II
Greenl White-fr. Goose	*Anser albifrons flavirostris*	II	–	W	0	0	14000	?	P	P	I,II,III	–	III	II
Barnacle Goose	*Branta leucopsis*	II	–	W	0	0	9000	?	P	P	I	–	II	II
Light-bellied Brent Gse	*Branta bernicla hrota*	II	–	W	0	0	16000	24000	P	P	II	–	III	II
Peregrine	*Falco peregrinus*	II	21	R	350	?	1000	?	P	P	I	–	II	II
Chough	*Pyrrhocorax pyrrhocorax*	II	21	R	650	900	2500	?	P	P	I	–	II	–
AMPHIBIAN														
Threatened Species														
Natterjack Toad	*Bufo calamita*	E	–	–	–	–	–	–	P	–	–	IV	II	–
Internationally Important Species														
Common Frog	*Rana temporaria*	II	–	–	–	–	–	–	P	U	–	V	III	–
FISH														
Threatened Species														
Sea Lamprey	*Petromyzon marinus*	I	–	–	–	–	–	–	U	U	–	II	III	–

River Lamprey	*Lampetra fluviatilis*	I	–	–	–	–	–	–	U	U	–	II,V	III	–
Brook Lamprey	*Lampetra planeri*	I	–	–	–	–	–	–	U	U	–	II	III	–
Allis Shad	*Alosa alosa*	E	–	–	–	–	–	–	U	U	–	II,V	III	–
Twaite Shad	*Alosa fallax fallax*	V	–	–	–	–	–	–	U	U	–	II,V	III	–
Killarney Shad	*Alosa fallax killarnensis*	E	–	–	–	–	–	–	–	U	–	II,V	III	–
Arctic Charr	*Salvelinus alpinus*	V	–	–	–	–	–	–	U	U	–	–	–	–
Pollan	*Coregonus autumnalis*	E	–	–	–	–	–	–	C	C	–	V	III	–
Smelt	*Osmerus eperlanus*	V	–	–	–	–	–	–	–	U	–	–	–	–
Internationally Important Species														
Atlantic Salmon	*Salmo salar*	II	–	–	–	–	–	–	C	C	–	II,V	III	–

Footnotes
1. RDB CATEGORY Ex – Extinct, E – Endangered, V – Vulnerable, R – Rare, I – Indeterminate, II – Internationally Important.
2. BEZZEL INDEX given for breeding birds only, see text for wintering birds.
3. STATUS (BIRDS) S – Summer visitor (breeding), W – Winter visitor, P – Passage migrant, R – Resident.
4. NUMBERS IN IRELAND (BIRDS) Most recent estimate for all Ireland; ? – numbers unknown.
5. NATIONAL LEGISLATION P – Protected species, U – Unprotected species, Q – Quarry species, C – Commercially exploited species.
6. OTHER LEGISLATION Listing of species in Annexes/Appendices of EC, European and international legislation. See Appendix V for details.
* Recently re-introduced but not yet established in the wild.

APPENDIX IV: NOTES ON INTERMITTENT BREEDING BIRDS

The following species have been recorded breeding or possibly breeding on a small number of occasions since 1970.

Black-throated Diver *Gavia arctica.*
Adults with flightless young seen on the coast of Donegal in the summer of 1990 (J.R. Sheppard).

Montagu's Harrier *Circus pygargus.*
A pair bred in Kerry in 1971. (A pair bred in Wicklow 1959–61) (Hutchinson 1989).

Osprey *Pandion haliaetus.*
Present in several breeding seasons since 1966 at undisclosed locations (Hutchinson 1989). A bird regularly seen taking fish in a densely-forested part of the North West in May and June 1992. The British breeding population reached 84 pairs in 1992 (G. Williams).

Dotterel *Charadrius morinellus.*
Bred on Nephin, Mayo in 1975 (Hutchinson 1989).

Savi's Warbler *Locustella luscinioides.*
Present at Shannon Airport Lagoon, Clare from 12–23 June 1980; one seen at Youghal, Cork from 17–23 June 1985 and joined by a second on 19 June (Hutchinson 1989). One seen at Ballycotton from 3–15 May 1988 (O'Sullivan and Smiddy 1989). There was no evidence of breeding on any of these occasions.

Lesser Whitethroat *Sylvia curruca.*
Single pairs bred near Newtown Mount Kennedy in Wicklow in 1990 and 1991 (H.J. Wilson) and on the Wexford coast in 1990 (Gibbons *et al.* in press). Birds have been recorded in at least two localities in Northern Ireland in the late 1980s, though there is no proof of breeding (R.A. Brown).

Hawfinch *Coccothraustes coccothraustes.*
There is a distinct possibility that this species bred in Ireland in 1991. Two adults and a juvenile were seen at Ballyvaghan, Clare, in September 1991 (O'Sullivan and Smiddy, 1992).

APPENDIX V: SUMMARY OF LEGISLATION RELEVANT TO IRISH VERTEBRATES

Legislation in Ireland

The principal statutes for the protection of wild vertebrate animals in Ireland are *The Wildlife (Northern Ireland) Order 1985* in Northern Ireland and *The Wildlife Act (1976)* in the Republic of Ireland. These statutes are administered by the Environment Service of the Department of the Environment in Northern Ireland and the National Parks and Wildlife Service of the Office of Public Works in the Republic of Ireland respectively.

Both statutes are wide ranging and comprehensive. Amongst their more important provisions are the protection of wild birds, their nests and eggs, some mammals (including cetaceans), reptiles and amphibians but not fish. They specify the species which may be hunted and specify and regulate hunting seasons. They specify the species which may be controlled under licence if proved to be causing a nuisance and the manner in which that control can be carried out. The legal status of each Red Data Book species is presented in the Species Account.

In Northern Ireland the Wildlife Order provides for the establishment of Wildlife Refuges for the protection of plants and animals. Areas of Special Scientific Interest and Nature Reserves can be established in Northern Ireland under the *Nature Conservation and Amenity Lands (Northern Ireland) Order, 1985* (amended in 1989).

In the Republic of Ireland the Wildlife Act provides for the establishment of state and private Nature Reserves for the protection of plants and animals, Refuges for Fauna for the protection of animal species and their natural habitats and Wildfowl Sanctuaries within which shooting is prohibited. In a High Court ruling in 1991 (confirmed by the Supreme Court in May 1993) Areas of Scientific Interest (ASIs) were found to have no legal basis because landowners had not been informed of the existence of ASIs on their property. All 1,800 or so biological ASIs are currently being re-surveyed and will be considered for designation as Natural Heritage Areas (NHAs) under an amendment to the Wildlife Act which will come before the Oireachtas in 1994.

Complementary legislation which has a role in vertebrate conservation provides for the control of water pollution, planning in the countryside, environmental impact assessment and the establishment of Environmentally Sensitive Areas (ESAs) in which traditional land management is promoted for the benefit of the wildlife and landscape. Some of these, such as the legislation enabling ESAs to be designated, have been produced in response to EC Directives.

Legislation in the European Community

EC Directive on the Conservation of Wild Birds (Directive 79/409/EEC of 2 April 1979) – elsewhere referred to as the 'Birds Directive'.

The 'Birds Directive' was adopted by the Council in 1979 and came into force in 1981. It directs all member states of the European Community to take measures to protect all wild birds and to preserve a sufficient diversity of habitats for all species naturally occurring within their territories, so as to maintain populations at an ecologically and scientifically sound level. Species whose status is a cause for concern are specifically identified for special conservation measures in Annex I. The Annex I species dealt with in this Red Data Book are indicated in Appendix III (see also in boxes under 'Birds Dir' in species accounts).

The 'Birds Directive' emphasises the conservation of bird habitats and it requires member states to designate networks of Special Protection Areas (SPAs). SPAs are now to be incorporated into the Natura 2000 Network (see below). Twenty one SPAs have already been designated in the Republic of Ireland and, at the present time, the Joint Nature Conservation Committee (UK) has just completed proposals for further designations in Northern Ireland and the Republic on behalf of the Department of the Environment (Northern Ireland) and the National Parks and Wildlife Service (Republic of Ireland).

EC Directive on The Conservation of Natural Habitats and of Wild Fauna and Flora (Directive 92/43/EEC of 21 May 1992) – elsewhere described as the 'Habitats Directive'.

This aims to '...contribute towards bio-diversity through the conservation of natural habitats and wild fauna and flora in the European territory of the Member States... ' and to restore and maintain these to a favourable conservation status. The core of this Directive is a coherent European ecological network of Special Areas of Conservation (SACs) set up under the title of 'Natura 2000' and covering certain habitat types (Annex I) and species (Annex II). The Directive also lists 'species of Community interest in need of strict protection' (Annex IV) and 'species whose taking in the wild and exploitation may be subject to management measures' (Annex V). The Directive also encourages Member States to conserve landscape features of importance to flora and fauna, such as river corridors, field boundaries, ponds and woodlands.

Other European Legislation

The Convention on the Conservation of European Wildlife and Natural Habitats (The 'Bern Convention').

This Council of Europe Convention was agreed in Bern in June 1979 and came into force in June 1982. It obliges contracting states to protect and conserve a wide range of plants and animals and their habitats, especially those listed as endangered or vulnerable. Contracting parties are encouraged to declare 'Biogenetic Reserves' as a contribution to the Convention's aims. To date eleven such reserves have been designated in the Republic of Ireland

and some of these – such as the Pettigo Plateau, Donegal (Hen Harrier) and Owenboy, Mayo (Greenland White-fronted Goose) – are relevant to the species covered by this Red Data Book.

The Convention also obliges parties "to promote national policies for the conservation of wild flora, wild fauna and natural habitats". It further states that these policies should give particular attention to "endangered and vulnerable species, especially endemic ones, and endangered habitats" (Lyster 1985). At the present time there are no explicit policies on wildlife and habitat conservation in Northern Ireland or in the Republic of Ireland under this Convention. The Red Data Book species covered by the "Bern Convention" are listed in Appendix III.

The Convention on the Conservation of Migratory Species of Wild Animals (The 'Bonn Convention').

This Convention provides for the conservation of migratory wild animals by giving strict protection to a number of endangered animals listed in its Appendix I, whilst providing the framework for a series of 'Agreements' between Range States for the conservation and management of its Appendix II species. The Red Data Book species covered by the 'Bonn Convention' are listed in Appendix III.

Following a meeting in Wexford in 1992 the International Waterfowl and Wetlands Research Bureau produced a draft international management plan for the Greenland White-fronted Goose and it is hoped this will be accepted and implemented under the terms of the 'Bonn Convention'.

International Legislation

Convention on Wetlands of International Importance especially as Waterfowl Habitat (The 'Ramsar Convention').

The 'Ramsar Convention', so called after the venue in Iran where the Convention was agreed in 1971, seeks to protect certain listed wetlands which are of international importance. Contracting parties are also exhorted to plan the 'wise [sustainable] use' of wetlands in all areas of policy planning and formulation. Criteria for identifying so-called 'Ramsar Sites' have been agreed at recent meetings of the Contracting Parties (Regina 1987 and Montreux 1990) and include factors such as numbers of waterfowl and other non-bird criteria such as the rarity or uniqueness of the particular wetland.

The protection afforded to wetlands by the 'Ramsar Convention' has significance for many of the Red Data Book species listed in this book, especially waterbirds. So far (October 1993) one site (Lough Neagh/Lough Beg) has been designated in Northern Ireland and 21 sites have been designated in the Republic of Ireland.

REFERENCES

GENERAL

Collar, N.J. 1987. Red data books and national conservation strategies. *World Birdwatch* 9(2); 6–7.

Curtis, T.G.F. and McGough, H.N. 1988. *The Irish Red Data Book. I Vascular Plants.* Stationery Office, Dublin.

Housden, S., Thomas, G., Bibby, C. and Porter, R. 1991. Towards a habitat conservation strategy for bird habitats in Britain. *RSPB Conserv. Rev.* 5; 9–16.

IUCN 1990. *The 1990 IUCN Red List of Threatened Animals.* IUCN, Gland.

McWilliams, B.E. (Ed.) 1991. *Climate Change. Studies on the Implications for Ireland.* Department of the Environment, Dublin.

Mitchell G.F. 1976 *The Irish Landscape.* Collins, London.

Munton, P. 1987. Concepts of threat to the survival of species used in red data books and similar compilations. In Fitter R. and Fitter M. (Eds.) 1987. *The Road to Extinction.* IUCN, Gland; 72 – 95.

NCC. 1990. *Handbook for Phase 1 Habitat Survey – a Technique for Environmental Audit.* Nature Conservancy Council, Peterborough.

Porter, R., Bibby, C., Elliott, G., Housden, S., Thomas, G. and Williams, G. 1990. Species action plans for birds. *RSPB Conserv. Rev.* 4; 10–14.

Rudge, A.J.B. 1984. *Conservation of Species of Wild Flora and Vertebrate Fauna Threatened in the Community.* Nature Conservancy Council GB / Commission of the European Communities. Vols. 1 & 2.

Scott, P., Burton, J.A. and Fitter, R. 1987. Red data books: the historical background. In Fitter R. and Fitter M. (Eds.) 1987. *The Road to Extinction.* IUCN, Gland; 1–5.

Stewart, N.F. and Church, J.M. 1992. *Red Data Books of Britain and Ireland: Stoneworts.* Joint Nature Conservation Committee, Peterborough.

Thompson, W. 1849–56. *The Natural History of Ireland.* Vols I–IV. London.

Whitten, A.J. 1990. Recovery: a proposed programme for Britain's protected species. *Nature Conservancy Council, CSD Report,* 1089.

MAMMALS

Bentley, E.W. 1959. The distribution and status of *Rattus rattus* L. in the United Kingdom in 1951 and 1956. *J.Anim.Ecol.* 28; 299 – 308.

Bentley, E.W. 1964. A further loss of ground by *Rattus rattus* L. in the United Kingdom during 1956–1961. *J.Anim.Ecol.* 33; 371 – 373.

Chapman P.J. and Chapman L.L. 1982. *Otter Survey of Ireland 1980 – 81.* The Vincent Wildlife Trust, London.

Corbet, G.B. and Harris, S. 1991. *The Handbook of British Mammals.* Blackwell, Oxford.

Deane, C.D. 1952. The black rat in the North of Ireland. *Ir.Nat.J.* 10; 292 – 298.

Evans, P.G.H. 1987. *The Natural History of Whales and Dolphins.* Christopher Helm, London.

Fairley, J.S. 1984. *An Irish Beast Book.* 2nd Edn. Blackstaff Press, Belfast.

Fairley, J.S. 1991. Whiskered bat in Galway City. *Ir.Nat.J.* 23; 425.

Lunnon, R.M. and Reynolds, J.D. 1991. Distribution of the otter *Lutra lutra* in Ireland, and its value as an indicator of habitat quality. In *Bioindicators and Environmental Management.* Academic Press 435–443.

McAney, C.M. 1987. Whiskered bat in Co. Galway. *Ir.Nat.J.* 22; 362.

McAney, C.M. and Fairley J.S. 1990. Activity of Leisler's Bat *Nyctalus leisleri* (Kuhl,1918) at a summer roost in Ireland. *Myotis* 28; 83 – 92.

Macdonald, D.W. and Barrett, P. 1993. *Mammals of Britain and Europe.* Collins Field Guide. HarperCollins Publishers.

Moffatt, C.B. 1938. The mammals of Ireland. *Proc.Roy.Ir.Acad.* 44B; 61 – 128.

Ní Lamhna, E. 1979. *Provisional Distribution Atlas of Amphibians, Reptiles and Mammals in Ireland.* An Foras Forbartha, Dublin.

O'Rourke, F.J. 1970. *The Fauna of Ireland.* Mercier, Cork.

O'Sullivan, P.J. 1983. The distribution of the pine marten (*Martes martes*) in the Republic of Ireland. *Mamm.Rev.* 13 (1); 39 – 44.

O'Sullivan, P.J. (in press) Bats in Ireland. *Ir.Nat.J.* Special Zoological Supplement.

Shiel, C.B., McAney, C.M. and Fairley, J.S. 1991. Analysis of the diet of Natterer's bat *Myotis nattereri* and the common long-eared bat *Plecotus auritus* in the west of Ireland. *J.Zool.Lond.* 223; 299 – 305.

Smal, C.M. 1991. *The National Badger Survey. Preliminary results for the Irish Republic.* Unpublished Report, Office of Public Works, Dublin.

Smiddy, P. 1987. Natterer's bat records from Cork and Waterford. *Ir.Nat.J.* 22 (5); 208.

Smiddy, P. 1991. Bats and bridges. *Ir.Nat.J.* 23; 425.

Smith, P. 1991. The 1991 Lundy ship rat expedition. *British Ecological Society Bulletin XXII* 4; 259–262.

Stebbings, R.E. and Griffith, F. 1986. *Distribution and Status of Bats in Europe.* Institute of Terrestrial Ecology, Monks Wood.

Walsh, P.M. 1988. Black rats *Rattus rattus* (L.) as prey of short-eared owls *Asio flammeus* (Pontoppidan) on Lambay Island, Co. Dublin. *Ir.Nat.J.* 22; 536 – 537.

WCMC 1989 *Draft Red Data Sheet – Wolf in Europe.* Unpublished. World Conservation Monitoring Centre, Cambridge.

BIRDS

Avery, M. and del Nevo A. 1990. The roseate tern – a special case for research. *Birds,* Autumn 1990; 26.

Avery, M. and del Nevo A. 1991. Action for roseate terns. *RSPB Conservation Review* 5; 54 – 59.

Batten, L.A., Bibby, C.J. Clement, P., Elliott, G.D. and Porter, R.F. (Eds.). 1990. *Red Data Birds in Britain.* T. & A.D. Poyser, London.

Bellamy, P. 1989. *Survey of Merlins and Hen Harriers in Northern Ireland in 1989.* Unpublished report. Royal Society for the Protection of Birds, Belfast.

Berrow, S.D., Mackie, K.L., O'Sullivan, O., Shepherd, K.B., Mellon, C. and Coveney,

J.A. (In prep). The Second International Chough Survey in Ireland. Paper submitted to *Irish Birds.*

Bezzel, E. 1980. *An Assessment of the Endangered Status of Europe's Breeding Birds and the Importance of their Biotopes as a Basis for Protective Measures.* Report (DOC. ENV/22/80) to European Commission.

Bibby, C.J. 1989. A survey of breeding wood warblers *Phylloscopus sibilatrix* in Britain 1984–85. *Bird Study* 36; 56 – 72.

Bibby, C.J. 1990. The hen harrier. *Birds,* Autumn 1990; 48 – 50.

Bibby, C.J. and Natrass, M. 1986. Breeding status of the merlin in Britain. *British Birds* 79; 170 – 185.

Bignal, E. (Ed.) 1989. *Choughs and Land-use in Europe.* Scottish Chough Study Group, Tarbert.

Blaker, G.B. 1934. *The Barn Owl in England and Wales.* Royal Society for the Protection of Birds, London.

Boyd, H. and Pirot, J.–Y. 1989. Flyways and reserve networks for waterbirds. *IWRB Special Publication* 9.

Brown, R.A. 1990. *Strangford Lough. The Wildlife of an Irish Sea Lough.* The Institute of Irish Studies and The Queen's University, Belfast.

Brown, R.A. and McAvoy, W. 1985. Nesting terns in Strangford Lough, 1969–84 – a review. *Irish Birds* 3; 33 – 47.

Bundy, G. 1978. Breeding red-throated divers in Shetland. *British Birds* 71; 199 – 208.

Butler, D. 1990. The incidence of lead shot ingestion by waterfowl in Ireland. *Ir.Nat.J.* 23; 309 – 312.

Cabot, D. 1990. *Studies on the breeding biology of the roseate tern* Sterna dougallii, *at Rockabill, Co. Dublin 1990.* Unpublished report. Irish Wildbird Conservancy, Dublin.

Cadbury, C.J. 1981. Nightjar census methods. *Bird Study* 28; 1 – 4.

Chapman, B. 1992. The tree sparrow. *IWC News* 70, Spring 1992; 10.

Clarke, R. and Watson, D. 1990. The hen harrier *Circus cyaneus* winter roost survey in Britain and Ireland. *Bird Study* 37; 84 – 100.

Comber, T. 1778 *Memoirs of...the Lord Deputy Wandesforde.* Cambridge.

Cooney, T. 1987. Little terns on the east coast. *Irish East Coast Bird Report* 1986; 43 – 45.

Cooney, T., Madden, B. and O'Donnell, M. 1991. *Irish East Coast Bird Report* 1990; 28–29.

Cotton, D.C.F. and Hillis, J.P. 1989. Black-necked grebes breeding in Ireland. *Irish Birds* 4; 72.

Cramp, S. 1985. *The Birds of the Western Palearctic. Vol. 4.* Oxford University Press, Oxford.

Cramp, S. 1988. *The Birds of the Western Palearctic. Vol. 5.* Oxford University Press, Oxford.

Cramp, S., Bourne, W.R.P. and Saunders, D. 1974. *Seabirds of Britain and Ireland.* Collins, London.

Cramp, S. and Simmons, K.L. 1977. *The Birds of the Western Palearctic. Vol. 1.* Oxford University Press, Oxford.

Cramp, S. and Simmons, K.L. 1980. *The Birds of the Western Palearctic. Vol. 2.* Oxford University Press, Oxford.

Cramp, S. and Simmons, K.L. 1983. *The Birds of the Western Palearctic. Vol. 3.* Oxford University Press, Oxford.

Crick, H., Dudley, C., Glue, D. and Turner, J. 1992. Breeding birds in 1990. *BTO News* 179; 8 – 9.

Cullen, J.P. 1991. The hen harrier in the Isle of Man. In *Birds and Pastoral Agriculture in Europe* (Eds: D.J. Curtis, E.M. Bignal and M.A. Curtis.) Scottish Chough Study Group, Tarbert.

Davies, M. 1988. The importance of Britain's twite. *RSPB Conservation Review* 2; 91 – 94.

Day, J.C.U. 1981. Status of bitterns in Europe since 1976. *British Birds* 74; 10 – 16.

Deane, C.D. 1979. The capercaillie as an Irish species. *Irish Birds* 1; 364 – 369.

Dennis, R.H., Ellis, P.M., Broad, R.A. and Langslow, D.R. 1984. The status of the golden eagle in Britain. *British Birds* 77; 592 – 607.

Elliott, G. (Ed.) 1991. *Roseate Tern News* No. 5. Royal Society for the Protection of Birds, Sandy.

Everett, M.J., Hepburn, I., Ntiamoa-Baidu, Y. and Thomas, G.J. 1987. Roseate terns in Britain and west Africa. *RSPB Conservation Review* 1987; 56 – 58.

Fairley, J.S. and Smal, C.M. 1989. Further observations on the diet of the barn owl in Ireland. *Irish Birds* 4; 65 – 68.

Farrelly, P. 1992. *Survey of Six Little Tern Colonies in Counties Louth, Dublin and Wicklow.* Unpublished report. Irish Wildbird Conservancy, Dublin.

Fox, A.D. 1991. History of the pochard breeding in Britain. *British Birds* 84; 83 – 98.

Fox, A.D. and Salmon, D.G. 1989. The winter status and distribution of gadwall in Britain and Ireland. *Bird Study* 36; 37 – 44.

Gibbons, D.W., Reid, J.B. and Chapman, R.A. (in press). *The New Atlas of Breeding Birds in Britain and Ireland: 1988–1991.* Poyser, London.

Glue, D. 1977. Feeding ecology of the short-eared owl in Britain and Ireland. *Bird Study* 24; 70 – 78.

Gochfield, M. 1983. The roseate tern: world distribution and status of a threatened species. *Biol.Conserv.* 25; 103 – 125.

Greenwood, J.G. 1984. Migration of dunlin *Calidris alpina*: a worldwide overview. *Ringing and Migration* 5; 35 – 39.

Hall, J.J. 1981. The cock of the wood. *Irish Birds* 2; 38 – 47.

Harrison, E.G. and Eadsforth, C.V. 1990. *A non-invasive approach for monitoring the exposure of barn owls to rodenticides.* Brighton Crop Protection Conference – Pests and Diseases – 1990.

Haworth, P.F. 1987. *Survey of west Galway.* Unpublished report. World Wildlife Fund, U.K.

Haworth, P.F. and Fielding, A. 1988. Conservation and management implications of habitat selection in the merlin *Falco columbarius* L. in the south Pennines, U.K. *Biological Conservation* 46; 247–260.

Haworth, P.F. and Thompson, D.B.A. 1990. Factors associated with the breeding distribution of upland birds in the south Pennines, England. *J.Appl.Ecol.* 27; 562–577.

Hirons, G.J.M. 1990. Review: *The Barn Owl in the British Isles: its Past, Present and Future* : by C.R. Shawyer. *Ibis* 132 (1); 140 –141.

Hotker, H. 1991. Waders breeding on wet grasslands in the countries of the European Community. *Wader Study Group Bulletin* 61, Supplement: 50 – 55.

Humphreys, G.R. 1978. Ireland's former premier breeding haunt of aquatic birds. *Irish Birds* 1; 171 – 187.

Hutchinson, C.D. 1989. *Birds in Ireland*. Poyser, Calton.

Jones, E. 1979. Breeding of the short-eared owl in south-west Ireland. *Irish Birds* 1; 377–380.

Kavanagh, B. 1991. *Irish Grey Partridge* Perdix perdix *Census 1991: Preliminary Report*. Royal College of Surgeons, Dublin.

Kennedy, P.G., Ruttledge, R.F. and Scroope, C.F. 1954. *The Birds of Ireland*. Oliver and Boyd, London and Edinburgh.

King, F. 1980. Red-necked phalaropes breeding at Akeragh Lough, Co. Kerry. *Irish Birds* 1; 540–541.

Kirby, J.S., Waters, R.J. and Prys-Jones, R.P. 1990. *Wildfowl and Wader Counts 1989–90*. Wildfowl and Wetlands Trust, Slimbridge.

Kirby, J.S., Ferns, J.R., Waters R.J. and Prys-Jones, R.P. 1991. *Wildfowl and Wader Counts 1990–91*. Wildfowl and Wetlands Trust, Slimbridge.

Kirby, J.S., Rees E.C., Merne, O.J. and Gardarsson, A. 1992. International census of whooper swans *Cygnus cygnus* in Britain, Ireland and Iceland: January 1991. *Wildfowl* 43; 20 – 26.

Lack, P. 1986. *The Atlas of Wintering Birds in Britain and Ireland*. Poyser, Calton.

Lecomte, P. and Sylvestre, V. 1991. Dry grassland birds in France: status, distribution and conservation measures. In *The Conservation of Lowland Dry Grassland Birds in Europe*. (Eds: Goriup, P.D., Batten, L.A. and Norton, J.A.) Joint Nature Conservation Committee, Peterborough.

McKeown, S. 1991 Eagle project launched. *IWC News*, 69 (Winter 1991); 4.

Marchant, J.H., Hudson, R., Carter, S.P. and Whittington, P. 1990. *Population Trends in British Breeding Birds*. British Trust for Ornithology, Tring.

Mayes, E. and Stowe, T. 1989. The status and distribution of the corncrake in Ireland, 1988. *Irish Birds* 4; 1 – 12.

Melville, D. 1973. Birds and salmon nets. *Seabird Report* 3; 47–50.

Merne, O.J. 1974. *A Guide to the Birds of Wexford*. South-East Tourism/Bord Failte.

Merne, O.J. and Murphy, C.W. 1986. Whooper swans in Ireland; January 1986. *Irish Birds* 3; 199 – 206.

Monaghan, P., Uttley, J.D., Burns, M.D., Thaine, C. and Blackwood, J. 1989. The relationship between food supply, reproductive effort and breeding success in arctic terns *Sterna paradisaea*. *J.Anim.Ecol.* 58; 261 – 274.

Nairn, R.G.W. 1986. *Spartina anglica* in Ireland and its potential impact on wildfowl and waders – a review. *Irish Birds* 3; 215–228.

Nairn, R.G.W., Herbert, I.J. and Heery, S. 1988. Breeding waders and other wet grassland birds of the River Shannon callows, Ireland. *Irish Birds* 3; 521 – 537.

Nairn, R.G.W. and Sheppard, J.R. 1985. Breeding waders of sand-dune machair in north-west Ireland. *Irish Birds* 3; 53 – 70.

NIBRC 1987. *Northern Ireland Bird Report 1982–85*. Northern Ireland Bird Records Committee, Holywood.

Noonan, G. 1988. The changing status of breeding merlins in counties Dublin and Wicklow. *Irish East Coast Bird Report* 1987; 51 – 60.

Norris, C.A. 1960. The breeding distribution of thirty bird species in 1952. *Bird Study* 7; 129 – 184.

Norriss, D.W. 1991. The status of the buzzard as a breeding species in the Republic of Ireland, 1977 – 1991. *Irish Birds* 4; 291 – 298.

Norriss, D.W. and Wilson, J. 1991. *Greenland White-fronted Geese in Ireland 1990 – 91.* Unpublished Report. National Parks and Wildlife Service, Dublin.

O Briain, M. and Farrelly, P. 1990. Breeding biology of little terns at Newcastle Co.Wicklow and the impact of conservation action, 1985–1990. *Irish Birds* 4; 149–168.

O'Connor, R.J. 1986. Biological characteristics of invaders among bird species in Britain. *Phil.Trans.R.Soc.Lond.* B 314; 583–598.

O'Flynn, W.J. 1983. Population changes of the hen harrier in Ireland. *Irish Birds* 2; 337 – 343.

O'Halloran, J., Myers, A.A. and Duggan, P.F. 1991. Lead poisoning in mute swans *Cygnus olor* in Ireland: a review. *Wildfowl – Supplement* 1; 389 – 395.

O'Meara, M. 1979. Distribution and numbers of corncrakes in Ireland in 1978. *Irish Birds* 1; 381 – 405.

O'Meara, M. 1986. Corncrake declines in seven areas, 1978–85. *Irish Birds* 3; 237 – 244.

Osieck, E.R. 1986. *Bedreigde en Karakteristieke Vogels in Nederland.* Nederlandse Vereniging tot Bescherming van Vogels, Zeist.

O'Sullivan, O. and Smiddy, P. 1987. Thirty-fourth Irish bird report, 1986. *Irish Birds* 3; 455–490.

O'Sullivan, O. and Smiddy, P. 1988. Thirty-fifth Irish bird report, 1987. *Irish Birds* 3; 609–648.

O'Sullivan, O. and Smiddy, P. 1989. Thirty-sixth Irish bird report, 1988. *Irish Birds* 4; 79–114.

O'Sullivan, O. and Smiddy, P. 1990. Thirty-seventh Irish bird report, 1989. *Irish Birds* 4; 231–257.

O'Sullivan, O. and Smiddy, P. 1991. Thirty-eighth Irish bird report, 1990. *Irish Birds* 4; 423–462.

O'Sullivan, O. and Smiddy, P. 1992. Thirty-ninth Irish bird report, 1991. *Irish Birds* 4; 571–610.

Owen, M., Atkinson-Willes, G.L. and Salmon, D.G. 1986. *Wildfowl in Great Britain.* Cambridge University Press, Cambridge.

Partridge, J.K. 1986. *Northern Ireland Breeding Wader Survey.* Interim Report. Royal Society for the Protection of Birds, Sandy.

Partridge, J.K. 1988a. *Northern Ireland Breeding Wader Survey.* Report to the Department of the Environment (NI), Belfast. Royal Society for the Protection of Birds, Sandy.

Partridge, J.K. 1988b. Breeding waders in Northern Ireland. *RSPB Conservation Review* 2; 69 – 71.

Partridge, J.K. 1989. Lower Lough Erne's common scoters. *RSPB Conservation Review* 3; 25 – 28.

Partridge, J.K. 1992a. *1992 Resurvey of Northern Ireland Breeding Wader Sites.* Report for RSPB, Belfast. Environment Plus, Crossgar.

Partridge, J.K. 1992b. Wetland birds and their habitats. In Proceedings of conference on *The Erne System, Sustainable Use of a Biological Resource, Enniskillen, 29–30 Oct 1992.* Institute of Biology, N.I. Branch, Belfast.

Partridge, J.K. and Smith, K.W. 1988. *Common Scoters: the Lough Erne Decline in an All-*

Ireland Context. Unpublished report. Royal Society for the Protection of Birds, Sandy.

Partridge, J.K. and Bellamy P. (In prep.) Status and food of the merlin *Falco columbarius* in Northern Ireland.

Pennant, T. 1766. *British Zoology* (Folio Edition). London.

Peterson, R., Mountfort, G. and Hollom, P.A.D. 1983. *A Field Guide to the Birds of Britain and Europe.* Collins, London.

Piersma, T. 1986. Breeding waders in Europe: a review of population size estimates and bibliography of information sources. *Wader Study Group Bulletin* 48 (Supplement); 1 – 116.

Potts, G.R. 1986. *The Partridge: Pesticides, Predation and Conservation.* Collins, London.

Reid-Henry, D. and Harrison, C. 1988. *The History of the Birds of Britain.* Collins in association with H.F. and G. Witherby, London.

Rüger, A., Prentice, C. and Owen, M. 1986. Results of the IWRB International Waterfowl Census 1967 – 1983. *IWRB Special Publication* 6, International Waterfowl Research Bureau, Slimbridge.

Ruttledge, R.F. 1966a. The present breeding distribution of the tree sparrow in Ireland. *Fourteenth Annual Irish Bird Report 1966*; 50 – 54.

Ruttledge, R.F. 1966b. *Ireland's Birds.* Witherby, London.

Ruttledge, R.F. 1975. *A List of the Birds of Ireland.* National Museum of Ireland, Dublin.

Ruttledge, R.F. 1978a. Greenshanks nesting in Ireland. *Irish Birds* 1; 236 – 238.

Ruttledge, R.F. 1978b. Red-necked phalaropes breeding south of latitude 53º48′ in Ireland. *Irish Birds* 1; 229 – 231.

Ruttledge, R.F. 1982. Red-necked phalaropes – a hitherto unrecorded case of breeding in Co. Mayo. *Irish Birds* 2; 196 – 197.

Ruttledge, R.F. 1987. The breeding distribution of the common scoter in Ireland. *Irish Birds* 3; 417 – 426.

Ruttledge, R.F. 1989. *Birds in Counties Galway and Mayo.* Irish Wildbird Conservancy, Dublin.

Scott, D., Clarke. R. and Shawyer, C.R. 1991. Hen harriers breeding in a tree-nest. *Irish Birds* 4; 413 – 417.

Sharrock, J.T.R. 1976. *The Atlas of Breeding Birds in Britain and Ireland.* T. & A.D. Poyser, Berkhamsted.

Shawyer, C.R. 1987. *The Barn Owl in the British Isles: its Past, Present and Future.* Hawk Trust, London.

Sheppard, J.R. 1978. The breeding of the goosander in Ireland. *Irish Birds* 1; 224 – 228.

Sheppard, J.R. (in press) *Ireland's Wetland Wealth – the Birdlife of the Estuaries, Lakes, Coasts, Rivers, Bogs and Turloughs of Ireland.* The report of the Winter Wetlands Survey, 1984/85 to 1986/87. Irish Wildbird Conservancy, Dublin.

Smal, C.M. 1987. The diet of the barn owl *Tyto alba* in southern Ireland with reference to a recently introduced prey species – the bank vole *Clethrionomys glareolus. Bird Study* 34; 113 – 125.

Smal, C.M. 1988. The American mink *Mustela vison* in Ireland. *Mammal Rev.* 18; 201–208.

Smal, C.M. and Fairley, J.S. 1984. The spread of the bank vole *Clethrionomys glareolus* in Ireland. *Mammal Review* 14; 71 – 78.

Stowe, T.J. and Hudson, A.V. 1988. Corncrake studies in the Western Isles. *RSPB Conserv. Review* 2; 38 – 42.

Stroud, D.A., Mudge, G.P. and Pienkowski, M.W. 1990. *Protecting Internationally Important Bird Sites.* Nature Conservancy Council, Peterborough.

Stroud, D.A., Reed, T.M., Pienkowski, M.W. and Lindsay, R.A. 1987. *Birds, Bogs and Forestry: the Peatlands of Caithness and Sutherland.* Nature Conservancy Council, Peterborough.

Summers-Smith, J.D. 1989. A history of the status of the tree sparrow *Passer montanus* in the British Isles. *Bird Study* 36; 23 – 31.

Thompson, D.B.A., Evans, A. and Galbraith, C. 1992. The fat bird of the barley. *BTO News* 178; 8 – 9.

Thompson, D.B.A. and Gribbin, S. 1986. Ecology of corn buntings (*Miliaria calandra*) in N.W. England. *Bull.Brit.Ecol.Soc.* 17; 69 – 75.

Tucker, G.M. 1991. The status of lowland dry grassland birds in Europe. In Goriup, P.S., Batten, L.A. and Norton J.A. (Eds) *The Conservation of Lowland Dry Grassland Birds in Europe.* Joint Nature Conservation Committee, Peterborough.

Tubridy, M. 1987. *The Heritage of Clonmacnoise.* Environmental Science Unit, Trinity College Dublin, in association with County Offaly Vocational Education Committee, Tullamore.

Ussher, R.J. and Warren, R. 1900. *Birds of Ireland.* Gurney and Jackson, London.

Voous, K.H. 1977. *List of Recent Holarctic Bird Species.* Academic Press for British Ornithologists' Union.

Walsh, A. and Merne, O.J. 1988. Barnacle geese in Ireland, Spring 1988. *Irish Birds* 3; 539 – 550.

Walsh, P.M. 1984. Diet of barn owls at an urban Waterford roost. *Irish Birds* 2; 437–444.

Walsh, P.M. and McGrath, D. 1988. *Waterford Bird Report 1976–1986.* Irish Wildbird Conservancy, Waterford.

Ward, D.P., Smal, C.M. and Fairley, J.S. 1986. The food of mink *Mustela vison* in the Irish midlands. *Proc.Roy.Ir.Acad.* 86B; 169–182.

Watson, D. 1977. *The Hen Harrier.* T. & A.D. Poyser, Berkhamsted.

Watson, J., Langslow, D.R., and Rae, S.R. 1987. The impact of land-use changes on golden eagles in the Scottish Highlands. *CSD Report No. 720.* Nature Conservancy Council, Peterborough.

Watters J.J. 1853. *The Natural History of the Birds of Ireland.* Dublin and London.

Whilde, A. 1979. Auks trapped in salmon drift-nets. *Irish Birds* 1; 370–376.

Whilde, A. 1983. The breeding waterbirds of Lough Corrib. *Brit.Ecol.Soc.Bull.* XIV; 155 – 157.

Whilde, A. 1984. The All Ireland Tern Survey – 1984. Unpublished report. Royal Society for the Protection of Birds, Sandy.

Whilde, A. 1985. The 1984 All-Ireland Tern Survey. *Irish Birds* 3; 1 – 32.

Whilde, A. 1986. *An Ecological Evaluation of Potential Areas in the West of Ireland for the Re-introduction of While-tailed (Sea) Eagles* Haliaeetus albicilla *L.* Unpublished report for Irish Wildbird Conservancy. Corrib Conservation Centre, Oughterard.

Whilde, A. 1987. *Pocket Guide to the Cliffs of Moher.* Appletree Press, Belfast.

Whilde, A. 1990. *Birds of Galway. A Review of Recent Records and Field Studies.* Irish Wildbird Conservancy, Galway.

Williams, G., Stowe, T. and Newton, A. 1991. Action for corncrakes. *RSPB Conservation Review* 5; 47–53.

Willughby, F. and Ray, J. 1678. *Ornithology*. London.

Winfield, D.K., Davidson, R.D. and Winfield, I.J. 1989. Long-term trends (1965–1988) in the numbers of waterfowl overwintering on Lough Neagh and Lough Beg, Northern Ireland. *Irish Birds* 4; 19 – 42.

Yalden, D.W. and Yalden, P.E. 1989. The sensitivity of breeding golden plovers *Pluvialis apricaria* to human intruders. *Bird Study* 36; 49 – 55.

REPTILES AND AMPHIBIANS

Arnold, E.N., Burton, J.A. and Ovenden, D.W. 1978. *A Field Guide to the Reptiles and Amphibians of Britain and Europe*. Collins, London.

Beebee, T.J.C. 1983. *The Natterjack Toad*. Oxford University Press, Oxford.

Beebee, T.J.C. 1991. *Natterjack Toad (*Bufo calamita*) Conservation in Ireland. Report of an On-the-spot Appraisal for the Council of Europe 4–7 June 1991*. Strasbourg.

Buckley, J. 1979. *Natterjack Toad Colonies in Co. Kerry 1979*. Unpublished expedition report.

Corbett, K. 1989. *Conservation of European Reptiles and Amphibians*. Christopher Helm, London.

Frazer, D. 1983. *Reptiles and Amphibians*. Collins, London.

Gresson, R.A.R. and O Dubhda, S. 1974. The distribution of the natterjack toad, *Bufo calamita* Laur, in County Kerry. *Ir.Nat.J.* 18; 97 – 103.

Mackay, J.T. 1836. The Natterjack (*Bufo rubeta*) occurs wild in Ireland. *Mag.Nat.Hist.* 9; 316 – 317.

O'Connor, P.G. and Jeal, F. 1984. Some notes on the distribution of *Bufo calamita* Laur, the natterjack toad in Ireland deriving from a survey conducted in 1975. *Bull.Ir.Biogeog.Soc.* 8; 30 – 41.

Persson, O. and Persson, E. 1980. The osteological analysis of the cremated and unburned bone material at a megalithic cemetary at Carrowmore, Co. Sligo, Ireland. In Burenhult, G. 1980. *The Archaeological Excavation at Carrowmore, Co. Sligo, Ireland. Excavation Seasons 1977–79*. G. Burenhults Forlag, Sweden; Appendix 1.

Raw, K. and Pilkington, G. 1988. Bringing back the natterjack toad. *RSPB Conservation Review* 2; 81 – 84.

FISH

Aprahamian, M.W. and Aprahamian, C. 1990. Status of the genus *Alosa* in the British Isles; past and present. *J.Fish.Biol.* 37A; 257–258.

Bahr, K. 1952. Beiträge zur Biologie des Flüssneunauges, *Petromyzon fluviatilis* L. *Zool.Jahrb.* 81; 408 – 426.

Behnke, R.J. 1972. The systematics of salmonid fishes of recently glaciated lakes. *J.Fish.Res.Board Can.* 29; 639 – 671.

Bracken, J.J. and Kennedy, M. 1967. Notes on some Irish estuarine and inshore fishes. *Ir.Fish Invest.Ser.B.* No.3; 4 – 8.

Dabrowski, K.R. 1981. The spawning and early life history of the pollan (*Coregonus pollan* Thompson) in Lough Neagh, Northern Ireland. *Int.Rev.ges.Hydrobiol.* 66; 299 – 326.

Dabrowski, K.R. 1982a. Seasonal changes in the chemical composition of fish body and nutritional value of the muscle of pollan, *Coregonus pollan* Thompson from Lough Neagh, Northern Ireland. *Hydrobiol.* 87; 121 – 141.

Dabrowski, K.R. 1982b. The influence of light intensity on feeding of fish larvae and fry of *Coregonus pollan* (Thompson) and *Esox lucius* (L.). *Zool.Jb.Physiol.* 86; 341 – 351.

Dabrowski, K., Murawska, E., Terlecki, J. and Wielgosz, S. 1984. Studies on the feeding of *Coregonus pollan* (Thompson) alevins and fry in Lough Neagh. *Int.Rev.ges.Hydrobiol.* 69; 529 – 540.

Ferguson, A. 1974. The genetic relationships of the coregonid fishes of Britain and Ireland indicated by electrophoretic analysis of tissue proteins. *J.Fish.Biol.* 6; 311 – 315.

Ferguson, A. 1975. Myoglobin polymorphism in the pollan (*Osteichthese coregoninae*). *Anim.Blood Grps.Biochem.Genet.* 6; 25 – 29.

Ferguson, A. 1981. Systematics of Irish charr as indicated by electrophoretic analysis of tissue proteins. *Biochemical Systematics and Ecology* 9; 225 – 232.

Ferguson, A. 1986. Lough Melvin. A unique fish community. Went Memorial Lecture 1985. *Occasional Paper in Irish Science and Technology*. Royal Dublin Society, Dublin.

Ferguson, A. and Fleming, C.C. 1983. Evolutionary and taxonomic significance of protein variation in the brown trout (*Salmo trutta*, L.) and other salmonid fishes. Systematics Association Special Volume No. 24: *Protein Polymorphism: Adaptive and Taxonomic Significance*. (Eds: Oxford, G.S. and Rallinson, D.). Academic Press, London.

Ferguson, A., Himberg, K.-J.M. and Svärdson G. 1978. Systematics of the Irish pollan (*Coregonus pollan* Thompson): an electrophoretic comparison with other Holarctic Coregoninae. *J.Fish.Biol.* 12; 221 – 233.

Fryer, G. 1991. *A Natural History of the Lakes, Tarns and Streams of the English Lake District*. Freshwater Biological Association, Ambleside.

Howes, C.A. and Kirk, B.R. 1991. A review of the smelt (*Osmerus eperlanus* L.) in the Humber and Tees estuaries, their tidal tributaries and the tidal waters of Lincolnshire. *Naturalist* 116; 27–30.

Hutchinson, P. 1983. *The Ecology of Smelt* Osmerus eperlanus *(L.) from the River Thames and the River Cree*. Unpublished Ph.D. Thesis, University of Edinburgh.

Hutchinson, P. and Mills, D.H. 1987. Characteristics of spawning-run smelt, *Osmerus eperlanus* L., from a Scottish river with recommendations for their conservation and management. *Aquaculture and Fisheries Management* 18; 249–258.

Kennedy, M. 1948. Smelt in the Shannon. *Ir.Nat.J.* 9; 151–152.

Lelek, A. 1980 . Threatened freshwater fishes in Europe. *Nature and Environment Series* No. 18. Council of Europe, Strasbourg.

Maitland, P.S. 1970. The origin and present distribution of *Coregonus* in the British Isles. In Lindsey, C.C. and Woods, C.S. (Eds.) *Biology of Coregonid Fishes*. University of Manitoba, Winnipeg; 99 – 114.

Maitland, P.S. 1972. Key to British freshwater fishes. *Freshwater Biological Association Scientific Publication* No. 27. Freshwater Biological Association, Ambleside.

Maitland, P.S. 1979. The status and conservation of rare freshwater fishes in the British Isles. *Proc.Inst.Br.Freshwat.Conf.* ; 237 – 248.

Maitland, P.S. 1980. Review of the ecology of lampreys in Northern Europe. *Can.J.Fish.Aquat.Sci.* 37; 1944 – 1952.

Maitland, P.S. 1990. *The Conservation of Rare British Freshwater Fish.* Nature Conservancy Council, Peterborough.

Maitland, P.S. and Campbell, R.N. 1992. *Freshwater Fishes of the British Isles.* Harper Collins.

Maitland, P.S. and Lyle, A.A. 1991. Conservation of freshwater fish in the British Isles: the current status and biology of threatened species. *Aquatic Conservation: Marine and Freshwater Ecosystems* 1; 25–54.

Maitland, P.S. and Lyle, A.A. In prep. Conservation of freshwater fish in the British Isles: proposals for management.

Maitland, P.S., May, L., Jones, D.H. and Doughty, C.R. 1991. Ecology and conservation of arctic charr, *Salvelinus alpinus* (L.), in Loch Doon, an acidifying loch in southwest Scotland. *Biol.Conserv.* 55; 167 – 197.

Moore, J.W. and Potter, I.C. 1975. A laboratory study on the feeding of the larvae of the brook lamprey *Lampetra planeri* Bloch. *J.Anim.Ecol.* 45; 699–712.

Moorehead, P.W. and Service, M. 1992. Capture of fish on screen of power stations in Northern Ireland. *Ir.Nat.J.* 24; 3–8.

O'Flaherty, R. 1684. *West or – Iar Connaught.* Hardiman, J. (Ed.) 1844. Dublin Archaeological Society, Dublin.

O Maoiléidigh, N. 1990. *A Study of Fish Populations in the Killarney Lakes.* Unpublished PhD Thesis. National University of Ireland, University College Dublin.

O Maoiléidigh, N, Cawdrey, S., Bracken, J.J. and Ferguson, A. 1988. Morphometric, meristic character and electrophoretic analyses of two Irish populations of twaite shad, *Alosa fallax* Lacépède. *J.Fish.Biol.* 32; 355 – 366.

Quigley, D.T.G. and Nolan, F. 1984. First record of char, *Salvelinus alpinus* (L.), for Shannakeela Lake, Maam Cross, Co. Galway. *Ir.Nat.J.* 21; 235.

Rosell R.S. 1993. *The Status of Pollan* Coregonus autumnalis pollan *Thompson, in Lower Lough Erne, Co Fermanagh.* Unpublished paper. Department of Agriculture (NI), Belfast.

Twomey, E. 1956. Pollan of Lough Erne. *Ir.Nat.J.* 12; 14–17.

Vickers, K.U. 1974. Occurrence of the smelt *Osmerus eperlanus* (L.) in the estuary of the Foyle. *Ir.Nat.J.* 18; 24.

Went, A.E.J. 1946. Irish freshwater fish. *Salmon Trout Mag.* 118; 248 – 256.

Went, A.E.J. 1953. The status of shads *Alosa finta* and *Alosa alosa* (Cuvier) in Irish waters. *Ir.Nat.J.* 11; 8–11.

Went, A.E.J. 1971a. The distribution of Irish char (*Salvelinus alpinus*). *Ir.Fish.Invest.* 6; 5 –11.

Went, A.E.J. 1971b. Interesting fishes from Irish waters in 1970. *Ir.Nat.J.* 17; 41.

Went, A.E.J. 1978. The zoogeography of some fishes in Irish waters. *Fishery Leaflet* 93. Department of Fisheries, Dublin.

Went, A.E.J. and Kennedy, M. 1969. *List of Irish Fishes.* 2nd Edition. Stationery Office, Dublin.

West, B., Cabot, D. and Greer Walker, M. 1975. The food of the cormorant *Phalacrocorax carbo* at some breeding colonies in Ireland. *Proc.Roy.Ir.Acad.* 75B; 285 – 304.

Wheeler, A. 1975. *Fishes of the World.* Ferndale, London.

Wheeler, A. 1978. *Key to the Fishes of Northern Europe.* Warne, London.

Whelan, K.F. 1989. *The Angler in Ireland.* Country House, Dublin.

Wilson, J.P.F. 1983a. The post-glacial colonisation of Ireland by fish, amphibia and reptiles. *Occ.Pub.Ir.Biogeog.Soc.* No.1; 53 – 58.

Wilson, J.P.F. 1983b. Gear selectivity, mortality rate and fluctuation in abundance of the pollan, *Corgenus autumnalis pollan* Thompson, in Lough Neagh, Northern Ireland. *Proc.Roy.Ir.Acad.* 83B; 301 – 307.

Wilson, J.P.F. 1984. The food of the pollan, *Coregonus autumnalis pollan* (Thompson), in Lough Neagh, Northern Ireland. *J.Fish.Biol.* 24; 253 – 261.

Wilson, J.P.F. and Pitcher, A.J. 1983. The seasonal cycle in condition in the pollan, *Coregonus autumnalis pollan* Thompson, of Lough Neagh, Northern Ireland. *J.Fish.Biol.* 23; 365 – 370.

Wilson, J.P.F. and Pitcher, A.J. 1984a. Fecundity of the pollan, *Coregonus autumnalis pollan* Thompson, in Lough Neagh, Northern Ireland. *J.Life Sci.R.Dubl.Soc.* 5; 21 – 28.

Wilson, J.P.F. and Pitcher, A.J. 1984b. Age determination and growth of the Pollan, *Coregonus autumnalis pollan* Thompson, of Lough Neagh, Northern Ireland. *J.Fish.Biol.* 24; 151 – 163.

Winfield, I.J., Tobin, C.M. and Montgomery, C.R. 1989. Ecological studies of the fish populations of Lough Neagh, Northern Ireland: a prelude to fisheries management. *Proceedings of the Annual Study Course of the Institute of Fisheries Management.* University of Ulster, Coleraine.

Winfield, I.J. and Wood, R.B. 1990. Conservation of the Irish pollan, *Coregonus autumnalis pollan* Thompson, in Lough Neagh, Northern Ireland. *J.Fish.Biol.* 37 (Supplement A); 259 – 260.

Wood, R.B. 1982. Lakes. In *Northern Ireland Environment and Natural Resources..* (Eds: Cruickshank, J.G. and Wilcock, D.N.) Queen's University, Belfast/ The New University of Ulster; 87–99.

Wood, R.B. 1989. Lough Neagh. *Occasional Paper in Irish Science and Technology.* Royal Dublin Society, Dublin.

Young, J.Z. 1981. *The Life of Vertebrates.* Clarendon Press, Oxford.

Zanadrea, G. 1962. Rapporti tra l'alto è il medio versante adriatico d'Italia nella biogeographia delle lamprede. *Boll. Zool.* 29; 727 – 734.

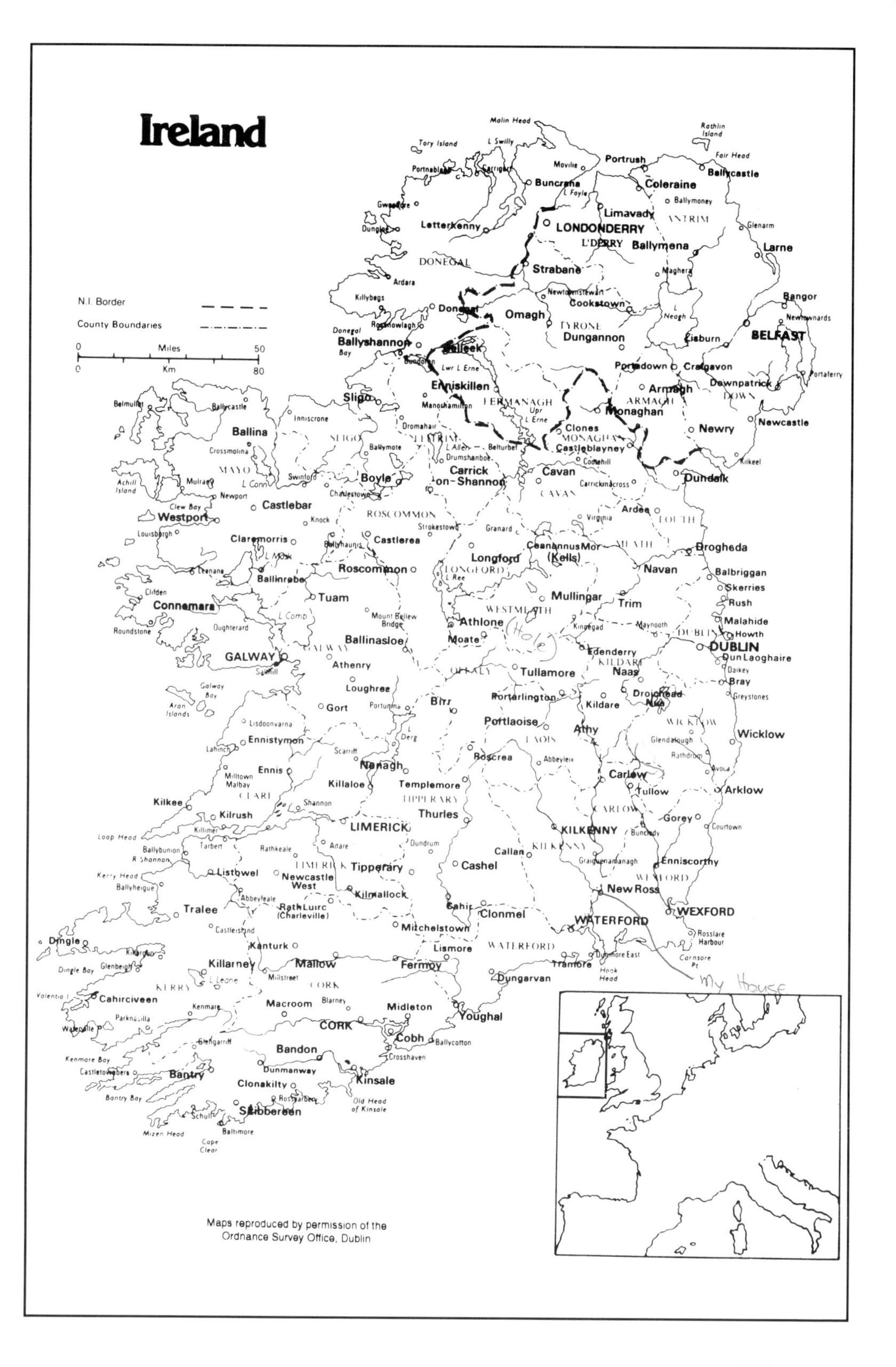

Maps reproduced by permission of the Ordnance Survey Office, Dublin

INDEX

Printed in Northern Ireland for HMSO Dd 8432295 C25 12/93 29254